WILDLIFE CONSERVATION

THE MACMILLAN COMPANY
NEW YORK • CHICAGO
DALLAS • ATLANTA • SAN FRANCISCO
LONDON • MANILA
IN CANADA
BRETT-MACMILLAN LTD.
GALT, ONTARIO

/ Wildlife Conservation

Ira N. Gabrielson

/ *Second Edition*

New York THE MACMILLAN COMPANY 1959

Second Edition, First Printing

The Macmillan Company, New York
Brett-Macmillan Ltd., Galt, Ontario

Printed in the United States of America

Library of Congress catalog card number: 59-10294

PREFACE TO SECOND EDITION

In revising this book an effort has been made to bring it up to date and to inject new ideas and new problems that have arisen and still preserve the original basic objective. No effort has been made to introduce all of the innumerable techniques that have been developed by wildlife specialists in the last few years. There is no field in natural resource management in which progress is more rapid, and any attempt to list techniques or details would be out of date before the book could be printed.

Definite effort has been made to retain the basic conservation philosophy and to analyze the basic factors that affect wildlife. In some cases changes have been made as a result of new methods and new concepts that have proven themselves, but no attempt has been made to introduce those that are still in the developmental or experimental stage.

IRA N. GABRIELSON

PREFACE TO FIRST EDITION

This book is not intended to be a complete analysis of all the complex factors that affect the conservation of wildlife. It is rather an effort to put into simple language the basic facts in this field and to emphasize that the various programs for the conservation of soil, water, forests, and wildlife are so closely interwoven that each vitally affects one or more of the others. All are phases of a single problem—that concerned with the restoration and future wise use of our renewable natural resources.

Although mention of many of the facts that affect wildlife populations must be omitted from a book thus limited in scope, an attempt is made to segregate some of the more important, particularly those that man, with his present knowledge, can alter, and to point to what can be accomplished thereby. The book may be considered as consisting of two parts—the first seven chapters showing the interdependence of conservation programs; and those remaining dealing with more specific problems of certain groups of wildlife, which are classified according to man's interest in them rather than on a purely biological basis.

In the attempt to simplify this presentation and yet make each chapter at least an outline of one major phase of the conservation problem, there is necessarily some repetition. This, however, has been unavoidable in trying to present clear pictures uncomplicated by the need for numerous cross references to other parts. In this broad presentation of the wildlife conservation field many biological details of the type with which those who are technically trained often delight to confuse their less erudite brethren are omitted.

Some will doubtless differ with me in the selection of the material included and also on the omissions.

Little is presented that is new or original. Rather this book attempts to strip down the complexity of contributions in the field of conservation to some of the more essential elements. Three concepts are considered to form the basis of the conservation movement: (1) That soil, water, forest, and wildlife conservation are only parts of one inseparable program; (2) that wildlife must have an environment suited to its needs if it is to survive; and (3) that any use that is made of any living resource must be limited to not more than the annual increase if the essential seed stock is to be continually available. These three concepts are the basis of present wildlife and forest conservation programs, and indirectly of all others. A multitude of details remains to be worked out, and it may well be that the techniques and tools of the future will need to be radically altered from time to time as knowledge increases and conditions change. It is my belief, however, that no amount of research and study will change these three basic concepts.

If this book succeeds in helping the general program of so restoring and managing our natural resources that this country becomes an increasingly better place in which to live, it will have accomplished its purpose. I desire here to express my appreciation and thanks to the technical workers of the Soil Conservation Service and the Forest Service who read and criticized the sections dealing with their respective fields, and to the numerous members of the staff of the Fish and Wildlife Service who rendered like service for the chapters dealing essentially with wildlife problems.

Ira N. Gabrielson

CONTENTS

Illustrations

HALFTONES

LINE DRAWINGS

1 / Conservation of Renewable Resources

Air, sunshine, soil, and water are the bases on which renewable, or organic, resources are built. Consequently, any practice that has an adverse effect on any of the four will be reflected in reduced production of the plants and animals on which man must depend for food and in the availability of habitable land. It is the power of these living things to grow and to reproduce themselves that constitutes the vital difference between the organic resources and those that are nonliving or inorganic. Recognition of this important difference will make it possible to develop and apply intelligent management.

Organic resources will grow and replenish themselves if given a chance by proper methods of protection, handling, and harvesting. Mineral and oil resources, on the other hand, once they are used, are gone forever and cannot be replaced. The stores of these important assets were assembled as the earth itself developed into its present form. The process of sorting and redistributing the minerals and of forming great beds of coal or pools of oil occupied periods of time that ran into hundreds of millions of years. Even coal and oil, now classed among the mineral resources, owe their origin to the abundance of the plant and animal life that thrived under special conditions far back in the earth's history.

The term "conservation," when applied to the two classes of renewable and nonrenewable resources, carries quite different meanings. The conservation of the inorganic, or nonrenewable, resources, such as coal, iron, copper, and oil, means sparing use with no waste. The conservation of organic resources implies use but only to an extent that will permit a continual renewal. It is with the conservation of the renewable resources that this book is concerned.

Comparable Importance of Inorganic and Organic Resources

Minerals, oil, stone, and other earth materials have been important to man in all stages of civilization, and as long as they are available they probably will continue to be of use to him. In his history man has developed from a primitive state through various types of culture. Named according to the material he has used for his tools, these stages have been termed the Stone Age, the Age of Bronze, and the Age of Iron. When man first began to shape tools he developed them from bits of bone or stone. It was only by slow and hard experience that he learned to work the metals that now play so important a rôle in his existence.

Despite his tools, his machines, and all his progress through all the stages of his history, from the primitive to the most highly civilized society, man has always been, and still is, dependent on plants and animals for sustenance and for protection against the elements. Fruits, vegetables, and seeds of many kinds are essential foods, and cotton, flax, and other plant fibers are indispensable for clothing. Meat, fish, shellfish, and many other products of the animal world enter into his diet; and wool, hair, and the skins of animals provide his clothing and shoes, as well as a multitude of other necessities.

Primitive man gathered such wild fruits, seeds, and tubers as chance provided and depended on his skill in the chase to obtain meat and fish. The various Indian tribes of this country, which had advanced to the new Stone Age when the white man first saw them, gathered the seeds of wild rice and of smartweed, the tubers of the groundnut and of the wapato or arrowhead lily, the bulbs of the wild camass, and the starchy roots of the bitterroot. Some tribes cultivated small patches of corn, potatoes, and other vegetables and developed great skill in hunting the variety of wild animals and birds that provided their fleshy food. The Sioux and other tribes waxed strong by utilizing the endless herds of buffaloes, which thundered across their grassy homelands, and the faraway Multnomahs traded for other articles or foods the wapato tubers that they harvested from the marshy lakes of their tribal lands along the Columbia River.

Modern man has developed numerous varieties of cultivated plants and so has a great range of foods from which to choose. Not satisfied with this, he has also developed a complex and rapid transportation system that enables him to enjoy not only the seasonal products of one community but of many, sometimes thousands of miles apart. He gets meat, eggs, hides, wool and other commodities from his domesticated mammals and birds, the many varieties of which he has developed the more fully to supply his needs. Animal and plant products from all over the world are available at a price to any community desiring them.

The combination of man's development of domestic varieties and of a mighty transportation system tends to obscure the fact that he still is dependent on plants and animals for his continued existence, and that if all plant and animal products were to become unavailable, human life would quickly vanish from the earth. While failure of mineral and other inorganic supplies would have the effect of disrupting modern industrial civilization, the withdrawal of organic supplies would exterminate the human race. Contrasting the relative importance of the two types illustrates the vital necessity of intelligently handling these resources.

Substitutes for iron, steel, copper, coal, and similar materials could be devised, and while possibly not so convenient at first, these might make it entirely possible for human society to continue. Charcoal and wood—the renewable fuels of the days before coal and oil came into general use—could again be widely used. In fact, many communities still find their chief source of heat in wood and wood products.

An increasing number of synthetic materials, mostly based on cellulose, which is of vegetable origin, are available for a wide variety of uses. Such diverse articles as railway-car wheels, the stress-bearing parts of automobiles, and finishing material for buildings are manufactured by the chemical treatment of wood fiber, or cellulose.

Chemists already know that when the available oil supplies become exhausted—possibly even before—it will be entirely possible to substitute for gasoline the alcohol or similar products that can be derived from vegetation. "Joy riding," therefore, would still be possible, though perhaps more costly than at present.

Thus it is seen that substitutes for various inorganic materials now used in everyday life could be derived from plants that can be grown or allowed to grow against the time when they will be needed.

The Basis of Life

The bodies of all plants and animals and the life processes within these bodies are all built around the chemistry of a comparatively few of the known elements. The most important of these are carbon, nitrogen, oxygen, and hydrogen. Smaller but indispensable quantities of calcium, sulfur, iron, phosphorus, potassium, sodium and other mineral elements are added by plants and through them are also available for animal needs.

The Carbon Cycle

Carbon is so important that organic chemistry, or the chemistry of living matter, is built about this element and the almost endless variety of its compounds with oxygen and hydrogen in the form of sugars, starches, and fats. When nitrogen is introduced and compounded with these three elements in still more complex combinations, proteins are formed. These four elements are basic to the food of all animals, including man. It is necessary to remember therefore a few of the fundamental facts concerning these chemical elements and the manner in which they are compounded, in order to understand the statement that air, sunshine, soil, and water are the bases on which organic life is built.

Carbon dioxide, a simple chemical combination of one unit of carbon to two of oxygen (CO_2), is the source of the carbon in living organisms. It is found in the air in the ratio of about three parts in 10,000 by volume. It is also found in solution in all waters, and in that form is available to aquatic plants.

Although carbon is so abundant, much of it is locked up in limestone, coal, oil, and other minerals. As we burn coal and oil, carbon dioxide is released into the air. Volcanic activity has the same effect. Most of the carbon dioxide supply in the main is maintained, how-

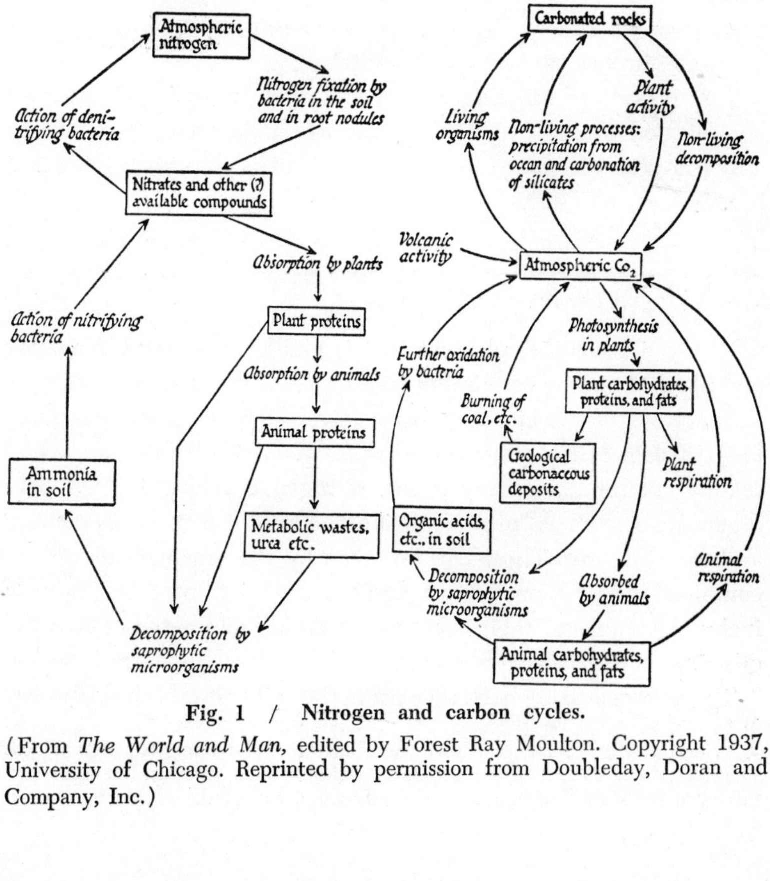

Fig. 1 / Nitrogen and carbon cycles.

(From *The World and Man*, edited by Forest Ray Moulton. Copyright 1937, University of Chicago. Reprinted by permission from Doubleday, Doran and Company, Inc.)

ever, by the activities of living animals. All animals in breathing take supplies of oxygen into their bodies and exhale carbon dioxide into the air. The process of decay of animal and plant tissues likewise releases carbon dioxide.

On the other hand, plants are continually taking in carbon dioxide and building it into carbohydrates. This phenomenon, known as photosynthesis, or literally "building by light," is the basic process by which plants capture and store the energy used by all living creatures. Without attempting to explain this process, which is still much of a mystery, it may be briefly described as the action by which plants containing the green coloring material chlorophyll combine the energy of sunlight with carbon dioxide and water into simple carbohydrates. From these, the more complex carbohydrates (sugars, starches, and fats) are built.*

This process of utilizing carbon and again releasing it creates a complicated cycle—which keeps the available quantity in the air and water at the fairly constant level that is necessary to sustain life.

The Nitrogen Cycle

Nitrogen is another element that is vitally necessary for animals and plants, but only certain forms of bacteria are capable of utilizing it directly from the air, despite its universal presence in abundance (80 per cent of the atmosphere is nitrogen). Unlike carbon, which readily combines in many forms, nitrogen is relatively inert. The organisms known as "nitrogen-fixing bacteria" can take this element and form nitrates. These can be taken by the green plants and be combined with carbon, oxygen, and hydrogen into proteins. Animals, including man, get their proteins by eating either these plants or other animals that have fed on them.

The nitrogen-fixing bacteria exist in the soil or establish themselves

* Certain types of bacteria have the ability to build inorganic material into simple foods for their own use without the aid of photosynthesis, but aside from this all other plant substances are manufactured as stated.

in nodules on the roots of leguminous plants. Such legumes as peas, beans, clovers, and alfalfa, because of their peculiar relationship to these bacteria, have long been cultivated to build up the nitrate content of the soil. All the time this is going on the decay of plant and animal tissue in the soil is releasing the contained nitrates into the soil to be used again by plants. The necessity of this return of plant and animal products to the soil is recognized every time manure is spread on the land or a green crop is grown to be plowed under as a fertilizer. This return of vegetable substances and animal wastes to the soil not only provides it with nitrates but increases its water-holding capacity, mingles usable combinations of mineral salts with it, and improves its physical condition.

During this process myriads of plants and animals live and die. The return of their bodies to the soil, through the complicated processes of decay, permits the limited usable supplies of some of these elements, including nitrogen, to be utilized over and over again.

It is thus evident that certain things found in the air, combined with the energy supplied by sunshine, are essential to plant life. Water also must be present. Soil holds these elements, together with other substances, in available form for the plant factories to build the world's food supplies.

Man's Influence on Natural Resources

The energy from the sun is beyond the present control of man, and the elements of the air are not greatly modified by his activities. He cannot add to the available sunshine nor can he control and direct that which is available except in a limited way. Neither can he change the constituent elements of the air, except very locally, nor their percentage relationships. About large cities, it is true that smoke and soot may pollute the air, but the effect is strictly local and the lifegiving oxygen and carbon dioxide and the valuable nitrogen still remain in about normal quantities.

Water and soil are in a different class. Man can and does disastrously affect them, sometimes directly and consciously and at other times indirectly and unconsciously. An example of direct and conscious harm to water is the dumping of raw industrial or municipal wastes into streams. Unconscious destruction of soil values has resulted from plowing the grasslands in the effort to develop them into fields for cultivated crops.

Since these two vital natural resources can be influenced and affected by man, separate chapters are devoted to outlining the relationship of soil and of water to conservation. A brief preliminary sketch is here inserted solely to show the intergradation of all of these elements into one cycle and to emphasize the fact that an intelligent conservation program must take into consideration all the factors that influence plant and animal production as well as the plants and animals themselves.

Soil

Soil is disintegrated rock that has been broken into particles of various degrees of fineness, sometimes transported by natural forces long distances, sorted out, deposited in layers or beds, and often torn up and rearranged again and again. Plant and animal remains are gradually incorporated into raw soils by the complicated processes already mentioned. Over long ages this has built up fertile soils that are capable of producing plant life in abundance. Fertile soil, built slowly through the ages, is a precious possession, but unfortunately one that can be dissipated or destroyed in a fraction of the time it took to form it. This country has not guarded its great soil resource and it faces the long and arduous job of restoration before vast areas can again be useful for human needs.

Water

Of the four great bases of life, water is the second that man can at least partially control. The need for water cannot be ignored; air and sunshine may be abundantly available, but with scanty moisture the soil will still be comparatively unproductive.

Some of the arid lands of the western states vividly illustrate the decisive importance of water. Air and sunshine are there in abundance and the soils are often rich in the mineral elements essential to plant life, yet plants exist sparsely and only in forms that have learned to store water for their own use, to hoard it as a miser does gold, and to survive with a minimum use of it during times of drought. Cactuses, for instance, with their often grotesque stems, are pulpy masses with high water-storage capacity, and have fewer surface pores through which water is transpired than plants growing in humid lands. Arid-land plants grow slowly and when death comes the incorporation of their substance with the soil also is slow. In the dry air of the deserts both plant and animal remains often mummify, the desiccated remains lying on the surface for long periods before they break down sufficiently to become humus. The absence or scarcity of water greatly retards the rate of the entire cycle of plant and animal production and soil building. Where water is abundant, plant life is more freely produced, the quantity depending on many factors, including soil fertility, temperature, and length of growing season.

Water, an absolute necessity for both plants and animals, is put to many uses by the human race. It may be either an obedient and powerful servant or, on the other hand, a terrible destroyer. Man himself has often been guilty of increasing its devastating effects.

In a country covered with vegetation the water is retained to a certain extent by the plant growth. Animal and vegetable débris, even that which has not yet been reduced to humus, takes up water and holds it. The vegetative cover also prevents the puddling and baking of certain types of soil into an armorlike surface that expedites the surface run-off. The porous surface of a soil well filled with humus, on the contrary, allows water to penetrate freely into the subsoils, and from these it is released gradually into springs and streams.

Where land is stripped of vegetative cover and soil is depleted of humus, a great volume of water must be carried away in a short time. This sudden running off of excess water results in floods that occasionally reach the proportions of major catastrophes.

In developing agricultural lands, many thousands of lakes, ponds, and marshes have been drained. Some of the drained areas became first-class agricultural lands; others were productive for a few years and then gradually declined; and still others were of little or no value at any time. The drainage attempts—uncoördinated in any way, and promoted largely or entirely by individuals or groups of individuals interested in exploiting definite areas of land—have given rise to a variety of problems, some apparent only in times of drought. Among the results are lowered water tables, accelerated run-off of precipitation, and the speeding up of destructive erosion, which often in a few years undoes the work of centuries of soil building.

Water as an animal-life habitat also supports many things of value to the human race. Fishes; mollusks such as clams and oysters; crustaceans including crabs, crayfishes, and lobsters; marine mammals such as walruses and seals; and aquatic and semiaquatic fur bearers such as beavers, muskrats, otters, and minks, from the earliest ages have supplied man with food, oil, and clothing. Many of them are still considered among the finest aquatic food products available to the human race, and the furs of some of the water-loving mammals are still among the most valuable natural products of the continent.

Man, in his effort to skim the economic cream from the land, has largely ignored these values. He has ruthlessly removed bodies of water that might have produced more value in fish, flesh, and fur than the drained beds ever have in agricultural products. This often resulted in gain for a few promoters but in slow ruin for the individuals who purchased the lands and tried to farm them and eternal loss to the communities about them. Other waters have been so polluted that all their aquatic life has been killed and their productive capacity temporarily impaired if not permanently destroyed. The profits have usually gone to relatively few individuals, while the losses have affected entire communities which may continue to suffer indefinitely. Much of this destruction can be repaired, but some of it has proceeded to such a stage that restoration will be a long and costly effort.

What of the Future?

The time may conceivably come when the last bit of iron will have been dug from the ground; the last pound of coal burned; the last drop of oil refined; and other inorganic resources exhausted. It is on these things that present civilization and industrial activity are largely based. Such resources were built in the earth through geologic times, and nothing that the human race has yet conceived can add to the total quantity now available.

It is interesting to look forward and speculate on a future without abundant mineral resources. Under such conditions the only supplies available to sustain human society will be agricultural crops, forestry products, meats, fish—in short the organic resources built about the chemistry of carbon and nitrogen. If this country continues depleting the soil, destroying the forests, and wasting the animal and plant life, it will, in time, become a poverty-stricken land inhabited by a constantly decreasing population facing a hopeless future. Such a fate has overtaken other lands with the exhaustion of their resources. It can well happen here.

To hope that the picture will not be quite so dismal, it must be assumed that the human race will be intelligent enough not only to stop the destructive processes that have been going on since the white man came to this country, but to reverse these processes before too late and start replacing the dissipated portion of the renewable resources.

Such a program would require, among other things, that submarginal lands that are rapidly deteriorating in value should be utilized for growing grass and trees, or they will shortly be as useless as millions of acres ahead of them have become. Agricultural practices that build soils must become the rule rather than the exception. This national reconstruction will require such a complete about-face with respect to the handling of water that it will be used as a valuable servant rather than a liability to be gotten rid of as quickly as possible. It will require a broadened vision, the development of new types of agriculture, and new social concepts.

Both the Small Watershed program, which became a federal activity with the enactment of Public Law 566 in 1954, and the so-called soil bank or conservation reserve program, enacted in 1956, give much promise for the future. Together they represent an almost complete reversal of governmental policy in dealing with land and water problems. In recent years the prolonged adherence to crop subsidies and the general lack of far-sighted planning in dealing with floods have been matters of deep concern to conservationists. These new programs, and the reasoning behind them, give some hope that a degree of sanity rather than political expediency may some day prevail in the federal land and water program.

Coördinate with timber and soil conservation, stocks of wildlife should be built up to play their part in soil-building mechanics and to serve as a reserve food supply as well as a source of outdoor recreation to a nation now so much in need of it. An increasingly valuable harvest can be expected as such a program becomes effective. At the same time the lands and waters can be put into condition to supply greatly increased quantities of organic products to meet the human needs when the mineral resources that have made this country industrially great are no longer abundant. This nation should be in a position to face that time with a vast forested area ready for full production and use on a crop basis. The agricultural areas should be highly fertile and capable of producing far greater quantities of useful products than now. The streams and lakes should be furnishing an annual yield of fishes and other products unhampered by pollution, and the agricultural, forest, and grazing lands a yearly harvest of wildlife as a by-product of their other uses. If such a program is carried out, this country may remain a prosperous land, capable of maintaining a great civilization, despite the exhaustion of many resources now regarded as indispensable.

Science has been able to turn wood and other organic materials into products that can be substituted in many cases for steel and other valuable metals. This industrial alchemy can be carried much further, and many articles now fashioned from metal may be made from something that can be grown as a crop. It will require a gradual evolution of a civilization based on available renewable resources, on things that can be managed, improved, and increased.

It could do no harm to the future of this country if all of the original forested areas could be restored as productive forests, with the exception of the better lands cleared for agriculture and those needed for residential and industrial use. If that part of the original grasslands not suited to agriculture also were restored for stock grazing and the production of meat and if other domestic-animal products became greater than current needs, the excess acreage could be devoted to the species of wildlife that require little care and comparatively little expenditure of money.

In its broadest social aspects, conservation of the organic resources means restoring to the highest possible level and maintaining in a state of high productivity those resources, including wildlife, that can be used on a crop basis to sustain human society.

This chapter has been devoted to outlining in a broad way problems involved in wildlife, forest, soil, and water conservation to emphasize the fact that all are really phases of one general problem. They are not so distinct and unrelated that any one of them can be successfully solved without due consideration of the others.

2 / Soil and Wildlife

Conservation of the renewable resources covers an exceedingly broad field and includes much more than saving birds or preserving other animals and plants. Its subdivisions are so intimately related that in discussing them it is necessary to separate the constituents. It is to be kept in mind, however, that each is only part of a complex system the elements of which are so closely associated that whatever affects one is very apt to have a far-reaching effect on one or more of the others.

Soil, water, air, and sunshine are basic essentials to life on the earth. While no more essential than the others, soil is a factor that man can improve or impair. It must be used wisely if this country is to continue suitable for human occupancy.

Soil Formation

Soil is no simple thing. Its basis is disintegrated rock, but that in itself may be nonproductive. The rock source of the soil determines the presence or absence of certain elements essential to plant growth. For example, soils originating from limestone are of higher fertility than those derived from sandstone or granite. Where soils are developed from the underlying rocks their natural fertility may, to a large degree, be dependent upon that factor. In those parts of the northern states that were once covered by glaciers, certain soils may have been transported long distances. These are the result of the age-long glacial action that ground up and mixed together many different types of rock from vast areas far distant from one another. They are generally of basically high fertility, though their actual productiveness may be governed by other factors. This is not a treatise on soil building, but some knowledge of that process is necessary to an understanding of the place of soil productivity and soil conservation in any program of wildlife conservation.

The agencies in rock disintegration, that is, the beginning of soil formation, are wind, water, ice, temperature, and vegetation. The continual action of these forces on the rocks tends to break them down into smaller and smaller particles. These are the raw materials of our present soils, but they require much modification before becoming usable by man. These crude soils may be transported and assorted by water or wind, or they may develop into arable soil locally without any movement.

The first plants that were capable of colonizing these rudimentary soils were no doubt very simple types, not the highly developed plants that we are accustomed to see and use. Plants of these simple types still live in raw soils. They are the pioneers and serve to modify crude soils so that other plants can gain a foothold. Bacteria, yeasts, algae, molds, fungi, and lichens were probably among the first kinds of plant life on the earth; at least they are among the most primitive that now survive. Among those that we first notice are mosses and lichens. The latter seem even to be able to dispense with the help of the pioneers, for, growing as they do on the face of rocks, they get most of their food from the air and from the water that falls upon their surface or trickles down the rocks. Their tiny rootlets, foraging for the minerals necessary to their life, slowly dissolve the surface of the rock and thus they aid themselves by breaking it down. Dust lodges among the lichens, and their older bodies persist as dry humus or, when wet long enough, decay, thus forming a soil containing both mineral and organic constituents. In this lichen-created base, the higher plants later get a foothold, and as they die they contribute more rapidly to the soil building. Animals attracted by them add their excreta and eventually their bodies to the complex. So the food material originally taken from the soil, air, and water, built by plants through the magic of sunshine into starches, sugars, proteins, and fats, and assimilated by animals for the varied uses of their own bodies, goes through the great wheel of life and eventually returns whence it came.

Every plant and animal, no matter how useless it may seem from other and more restricted viewpoints, serves a useful purpose in the mechanism of soil building. Intricate as is the soil-building process throughout, no part of it is more complex than that concerned with the incorporation of plant and animal bodies. These bodies are broken down by insects and worms, by microscopic animals and bacteria—a living community recruited for this service. In fact, the soil itself is a living community of minute forms of life, millions upon millions of individuals, all involved in its modification.

The accumulation of vegetable and animal débris and its incorporation into the soil is nature's slow but continuous process of increasing productivity. It provides the humus that makes the soil friable and easily tillable and gives it power to absorb and hold the great quantities of water necessary to both plant and animal existence. The lapse of time and the efforts of nature required for the formation of a soil capable of producing agricultural crops are vast and impressive. It has been estimated that it takes as much as three hundred to a thousand years or more for natural processes to build one inch of productive topsoil.

The growth of vegetation as the soil becomes more fertile increases in density up to the limits of the available moisture. The vegetative cover holds the soil in place, stabilizes its levels, and conserves the topsoil—the most productive part of the land. This never-ending process of soil building and the development on the soil of an increasingly complex plant and animal community had been going on for ages before the white man came to this country. On his arrival he found a continent of predominantly rich soils, vast forests, and grassy plains and prairies, all populated by an abundance of living things.

Soil Erosion

The development of soils through the leisurely processes of rock weathering and the incorporation of organic material has always been frustrated to some extent by the destructive process of geologic erosion. Soil is removed by rushing water and sweeping wind. Some of the material thus transported reaches the oceans; part of it is deposited by stream overflow to form a rich alluvium. Generally, under a protective cover of vegetation, this kind of surface removal goes on so slowly that soil is probably built as fast as it is removed, so that a balance is maintained and topsoil seemingly endures permanently. Thus geologic erosion may be a beneficial process. At any rate, man is little concerned with such long-time processes. In contrast, however, he is responsible for accelerated soil erosion—the greatly speeded-up removal of soil following his stripping off of the cover of trees, grass, and other forms of vegetation that give protection to land under natural conditions.

As the white man explored this country he found the Atlantic seaboard and the areas westward to the Mississippi Valley largely forested and densely covered with vegetation. Beyond the forests were the tall-grass prairies, and still farther west the short-grass plains, all with vegetative covers maintaining characteristic environmental conditions.

In order to till the soil, man cut down the forests and plowed up the grassland, rudely interrupting ground conditions developed through the soil-building processes that had been going on for ages. In many instances the forests were completely wasted. Trees that were girdled and burned at "log-rollings" would now be worth many times the value of the crops produced on some of the land cleared by this method. The pioneers in the new country were land crazy, intensely interested in land speculation, land clearing, and the development of farming enterprises across the frontier. The continent seemed inexhaustible, and the tide of population flowing westward had no experience on which to base any course different from that followed. As a result of the few score years of land exploitation, we now have an ever increasing area on which the destruction of vegetative cover has accelerated soil erosion to the point where all or a large part of the original topsoil, built through geologic ages, is

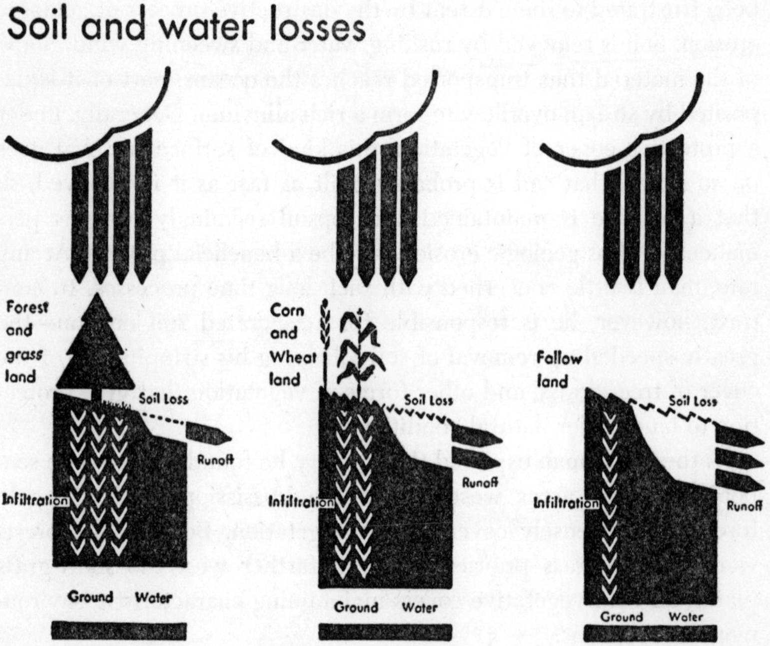

Fig. 2 / (From *Little Waters* by H. S. Person, et al., 1935.)

being dissipated. In places its plant foods have been taken out in the form of harvested crops, and continual recropping of the same land has exhausted a large part of its fertility. Both soil and soil fertility have been destroyed by erosion as the result of plowing steep sloping lands and accelerating the run-off of water. Some specialists estimate that the Mississippi River alone carries 730,000,000 tons of soil into the Gulf of Mexico each year.

Man has drained lakes and marshes that constituted the natural storage reservoirs of flood waters and served to maintain soil water tables; he has ditched millions of acres of land with open or tiled drains and straightened hundreds of miles of streams to facilitate the run-off or to put more land under cultivation. These activities in many places have contributed to destructive erosion.

The plowing up of the grasslands in areas like the Great Plains has resulted in the acceleration of destructive erosion by wind action. In the Plains country the rainfall was always too scanty and uncertain to sustain a protecting forest growth, but the grass served the same purpose. It held the soil in place, built up its humus content, and promoted the infiltration of water. When this cover was gone, the soil was exposed to the erosive action of the strong winds characteristic of the region. Specialists tell us that a single dust storm on May 12, 1934, carried 300,000,000 tons of fertile topsoil off the Plains area. This is only one of the many such storms that have wrought permanently destructive effects on these lands. It has been estimated that throughout the country water and wind erosion, together, remove beyond use 3,000,000,000 tons of soil annually.

There are in the United States today about 100,000,000 acres of formerly cultivated land on which erosion has gone so far that profitable crop production is no longer possible. Much of it stands abandoned, enormous gullies cut through it by the rain water that races over the bared surface. Another 100,000,000 acres have been impaired to varying degrees, and the process is getting under way on still another 100,000,000 acres of farmland. Additional damage has taken place on millions of acres of western range land. The extent of this devastation may be realized if one remembers that each of these 100,000,000 acre areas is equivalent to the land area of California, now the third largest state in the Union.

What is the bearing of all this on wildlife conservation? There is a popular belief that land of no use for anything else is good enough for wildlife. This thought arises largely no doubt from the fact that wildlife has frequently been crowded into such places as a last stand in the face of increasingly intensive use of the land by man. Wildlife requires suitable food and shelter just as does any domestic animal and can exist only precariously and in small numbers on the waste lands ruined by erosion. In bitter truth, these lands have been seriously impoverished or destroyed not only for farming and grazing but also to a very large extent for the occupancy of any form of life that is useful to man. Owing to wanton improvidence, a great area must go through a long process of rebuilding before it can again sustain any life in abundance.

What Must Be Done to Rebuild the Soil

It is obvious that a system of handling soils far different from that which has prevailed must be developed if destructive erosion is to be halted, to say nothing of its being replaced by a soil-improvement program.

The vegetative cover must be restored. Forests and grass must grow again on lands too steep, too poor, or too arid to produce agricultural crops profitably in the average year—not in the exceptional year that too frequently is the criterion upon which agricultural hopes are based.

The water that falls on the land must be put to profitable use rather than treated as a menace to be hurried away to the great rivers and the sea. Proper utilization of water is certainly an integral part of an erosion-control program.

Better agricultural practice must be followed on the lands that are to be cultivated—one that will control erosion and thus not only conserve the remaining soil fertility but also, so far as possible, again put to work for us the biological processes of soil building.

Most important of all the devices for soil-erosion control is the revegetation of eroding lands. Any sort of vegetation—even the most troublesome weed—is preferable to bare soil exposed to the action of wind or water. In areas of adequate rainfall trees and shrubs are the most valuable and easily established types of vegetation. Erosion-control specialists prefer those that have a great mass of small roots to serve the double purpose of holding the soil mechanically in place and opening it up to allow ready infiltration of water. The leaves and other accumulated débris from trees and shrubs soon begin to form a litter on the ground and this litter, as it grows in depth, becomes

EROSION CONTROL CAN HELP WILDLIFE

Plate 1 / In two years an earth dam and black locust plantings result in a growth that helps to control a gully and provide habitat for wildlife.

(Soil Conservation Service photos: IA207 by Franklin Pugh; IA207b, photographer unknown.)

CHECK DAMS HELP EROSION CONTROL AND WILDLIFE

Plate 2 / **An earth dam with a drop inlet (above) stops a gully and creates a small pond, and wire dams (below) hold silt in a gully and make it easier to establish vegetation that will stabilize the gully and provide cover and food for wildlife.**

(Soil Conservation Service photos: NEB232 by Richard Hufnagle; IA340 by George V. Gideon.)

WE NEED OUR LAKES AND MARSHES

Plate 3 / The open-water area of the Medicine Lake National Wildlife Refuge in Montana (above) and the marshes of the Sacramento Refuge in California (below) illustrate two important types of wildlife habitat.

(Fish and Wildlife Service photos: B57960 by Erling R. Quortrup; B58859 by Peter J. Van Huizen.)

DAMS HELP IN WILDLIFE RESTORATION

Plate 4 / Small dams like that on the Pablo National Wildlife Refuge in Montana (above) and water storage on larger units like the lake at the Wildfang Waterfowl Project in North Dakota (below) improve wildlife conditions.

(Fish and Wildlife Service photos: B54058 by Kenneth F. Roahen; B48132 by Frank Van Kent.)

WATER AREAS PROVIDE FOOD FOR WILDLIFE

Plate 5 / The emergent wildrice *(Zizania aquatica)* **on the lower Souris National Wildlife Refuge in North Dakota (above) and the submerged pondweed** *(Potamogeton perfoliatus* **var.** *bupleuroides)* **(below) illustrate the fresh-water aquatic plants that provide food for waterfowl.**

(Fish and Wildlife Service photos: B53422 by C. J. Henry; B42140 by F. M. Uhler.)

DUCKS AND GEESE ARE *WATER*FOWL

Plate 6 / The snow geese at the Sacramento National Wildlife Refuge in California (above) and the canvasback ducks at Lake Merritt in Oakland, Calif. (below), are examples of the waterfowl concentrations that are enjoyed annually wherever the birds can find suitable surroundings.

(Fish and Wildlife Service photos: B58863 by Peter J. Van Huizen; B43047 by Hugh M. Worcester.)

GOOD FISHING REQUIRES GOOD WATER

Plate 7 / Clean and plentiful water makes it possible for such fish as the spawning trout in Yosemite National Park (below) to multiply, and the fisherman's reward comes with such catches as the bass (above) taken from Lake Mead at the Boulder Dam Recreational Area.

(United States Department of the Interior photos by George A. Grant and Allen Reinhart.)

GOOD WATER AREAS PRODUCE FUR

Plate 8 / The beaver, one of the many valuable fur animals that are dependent on good water conditions, creates its own dam (below) and helps conserve the water supply.

(Fish and Wildlife Service photos: B4544M by Ben East; B3292M, photographer unknown.)

increasingly effective in slowing down the rush of water from the land and in increasing the water-holding capacity of the soil.

In the semiarid, wind-swept areas, where the protective plant cover is entirely gone from numerous places, the program of establishing vegetation is more difficult. Contour furrows conserve rainfall and thus help reëstablish protective vegetation. Even the Russian thistle, considered a pestiferous weed in many places, has been found useful in stopping wind erosion on the Great Plains, where it is difficult to get any vegetation started.

Steep slopes, gullies, and waste places generally should be covered with vegetation as quickly as possible. Any kind will help, but if it can also be some type of useful vegetation, the community obviously will be the gainer. In the choice of planting material, wildlife may well be considered. Many trees and shrubs and perennial and annual plants that have the hardiness, adaptability, and root systems needed for erosion-control plantings also furnish valuable food and cover for wildlife. Obviously, if these are planted, two useful purposes will be served. In agricultural areas the choice of such plant forms may result in attracting several kinds of birds or mammals that otherwise would be absent.

Where gully erosion has proceeded far, mechanical aids in slowing up the rush of the storm waters may be a necessary preliminary to the reëstablishment of vegetation. The installation of baffleboards, small check dams, brush dams, and other devices is first frequently necessary. These serve to check washing and to impound small pools that fill with sediment, forming flats on which vegetation may be renewed. By such means a gully, if not too deep, may gradually be filled. There are areas, particularly in the southeastern and southwestern states, where gully systems have spread so widely that there is little that man can do in the way of control except so far as possible encourage revegetation. In such severely eroded areas, locusts, junipers, and pines are among the trees most likely to establish and maintain themselves.

On lands that must remain in cultivation, methods can be employed that will greatly reduce the loss of valuable soil through erosion. Lands not too steep for agricultural use but yet steep enough to erode badly if planted to tilled crops should be kept so far as possible in hay and pasture crops. Clover, alfalfa, and lespedeza are among the soil-building plants that are favored for this use; all of them have root systems that carry nitrogen-fixing bacteria and penetrate soils deeply. On less sloping lands contour plowing, that is, plowing at right angles to the slope of the land, is effective in preventing washing and in forcing more water into the soil. Conversely, plowing downhill creates in every furrow a tiny channel that accelerates run-off and increases the loss from erosion.

Where steeper slopes must be farmed, terracing will check the flow of water, reduce erosion, and store rainfall in the soil. Not only will terraces do this but they also will prevent the formation of streamlets that in a heavy rain may grow formidable and destructive on a relatively short slope.

Strip planting is another erosion-control device of an interesting and somewhat different type. Perennial grasses or forage crops are planted across the slope of the land, usually on the steeper pitches, and tilled crops, as corn, cotton, and tobacco, are planted in the intervening spaces and also in rows at right angles to the grade. The gain in conserving soil and storing water is so much greater than the loss caused by inconvenience of tillage that the practice is rapidly spreading.

The restoration of natural lakes and marshes and the construction of small artificial reservoirs as water-control works may be quite important in a soil-conservation program. Such reservoirs retard the run-off of storm waters, force more water into the ground and so maintain the supply of ground water, and tend to maintain springs and streams in periods of dry weather.

To the extent that proper soil-conservation practices are adopted in the eroding agricultural areas we may expect gradual improvement in vegetative production. This may well be reflected in improved living conditions for the human race and for many wild creatures. It will put nature's geological and biological factory back at the task of soil building in the expanding waste lands, turning them again to a useful purpose.

3 / Water Conservation

Water is one of the great agencies of soil erosion and is also one of the four vital bases of plant and animal life. Of these, soil and water are the only ones that at present can be controlled to any considerable degree by man. The conservation of both of these is basic not only to wildlife conservation but to the needs of the human race as well. The great productive regions of the world are found only where there is an abundance of rainfall; the desert areas are in regions so scantily or unevenly watered that crops of economic importance or the plant cover essential to wildlife cannot exist in sufficient quantities to sustain large populations.

In considering water conservation close attention must be given to the water cycle, which may be described as follows: Water falls from the clouds to the ground in the form of rain or snow. Part of it runs away on the surface. Some of it penetrates to varying depths, depending on characteristics of the soil. Part of this comes out in springs and streams and part of it, penetrating to deeper levels, may come out only in the greater lakes or oceans. Some of the ground water is absorbed by vegetation and then transpired and some is evaporated from the soil. Whether transpired by plants, evaporated from the surface of the ground near the spot where it fell or at some other point after traversing devious channels, or rising as vapor from the surface of streams, ponds, lakes, or the sea, the water returns to the clouds to be again precipitated on some perhaps distant part of the earth as rain, snow, sleet, or hail. (See Fig. 3.)

The character and extent of this precipitation, as well as its seasonal distribution and the water-retaining capacity of the soil, are among the important factors determining the distribution and abundance of vegetation and consequently also of animals. The abun-

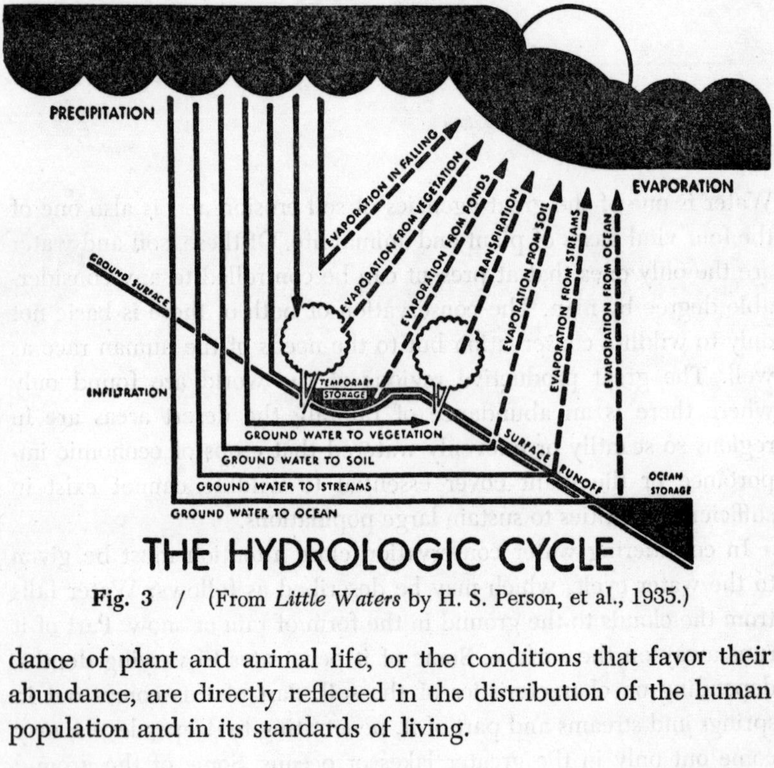

Fig. 3 / (From *Little Waters* by H. S. Person, et al., 1935.)

dance of plant and animal life, or the conditions that favor their abundance, are directly reflected in the distribution of the human population and in its standards of living.

Original Conditions

The original conditions in this country as undisturbed by man resulted from comparatively stabilized relations between soil fertility, availability and distribution of water, and vegetation. In areas with fertile soil and adequate rainfall, forests prevailed. Where the rainfall on productive soil was less than the quantity needed to produce forests, rank growths of tall grasses and other herbaceous plants flourished. On soils still good, but having scantier rainfall, shorter grasses and more sparse vegetation occurred. This type of environment gradually changed with increased aridity to semidesert and desert, where the sparse vegetation consisted only of plants with special adaptations for water conservation.

In cycles of drought when during several years the precipitation may be below normal, the grasslands tend to invade the forests, and the converse is true when precipitation is above normal. Evidence of such a shift may be seen at the present time in western mountains, where yellow pines twenty to thirty years of age or more that had crept out into the open lands during adequate rainfall cycles later died for lack of water.

The eastern United States was largely forested. Farther west grasslands predominated. Through the glaciated northern states in both areas innumerable lakes, marshes, and ponds dotted the landscape. These depressions, which were filled by melting snows and early spring rains, served as storage reservoirs and then excess of evaporation over precipitation during the summer months gradually lowered their water levels. Water tables were maintained at or near the maximum level by natural storage in forests and grasslands, and in swamps, marshes, and lakes. Absorption of water into the soil was promoted and the run-off diminished by the fact that the surface of the ground was covered with vegetation and the topsoil filled with humus.

Changes by Man

The forests, themselves an important water conservation and distribution agency, were soon cut down by man. The prairies and plains were plowed and marshes were drained to produce in some cases good agricultural ground and in others land of little or no value. The entire agricultural effort was devoted to clearing land

and to hastening the flow of water from it, by draining marsh and water areas, digging open ditches, and putting in thousands of miles of tiled drains. Streams were straightened and deepened until many of them run through narrow, straight ditches. Under original conditions the meandering streams held back the flow and helped to maintain water in the soil well toward its normal carrying capacity.

The tendency of man's efforts, particularly in the northern Mississippi Valley, where drainage and development of farm land have been carried to the greatest extreme, has been toward getting rid of water rather than using it. Not merely hundreds, but literally thousands of lakes, ponds, and marshes, have been drained, sometimes by very costly engineering operations.

Floods and Their Origin

Much speculation has been aroused in recent years by the disastrous floods that seem to occur with greater frequency and increasing severity. There were floods in this country before the days of agriculture, and there will continue to be floods as long as there is sudden and excessive precipitation. There is no question, however, in the minds of biologists, soil conservationists, and engineers that the tremendous ditching and drainage programs, together with the removal of vegetation, have appreciably increased the severity of floods. A few drainage projects or the scalping of land on part of the farms in a watershed would not have any great influence in increasing the flood run-off, but the total effect of rushing the water from thousands of square miles into the main river channels is enormous.

If excessive precipitation should occur simultaneously over the basins of all the principal northern tributaries of the Mississippi River, the flood crests farther down would be unprecedented. Building and maintaining the vast levees on the lower stretches of the main river for the protection of towns and farming lands is exceedingly costly. Many biologists and students of the water cycle believe that levee construction, although necessary, attacks the flood-control problem at the wrong end.

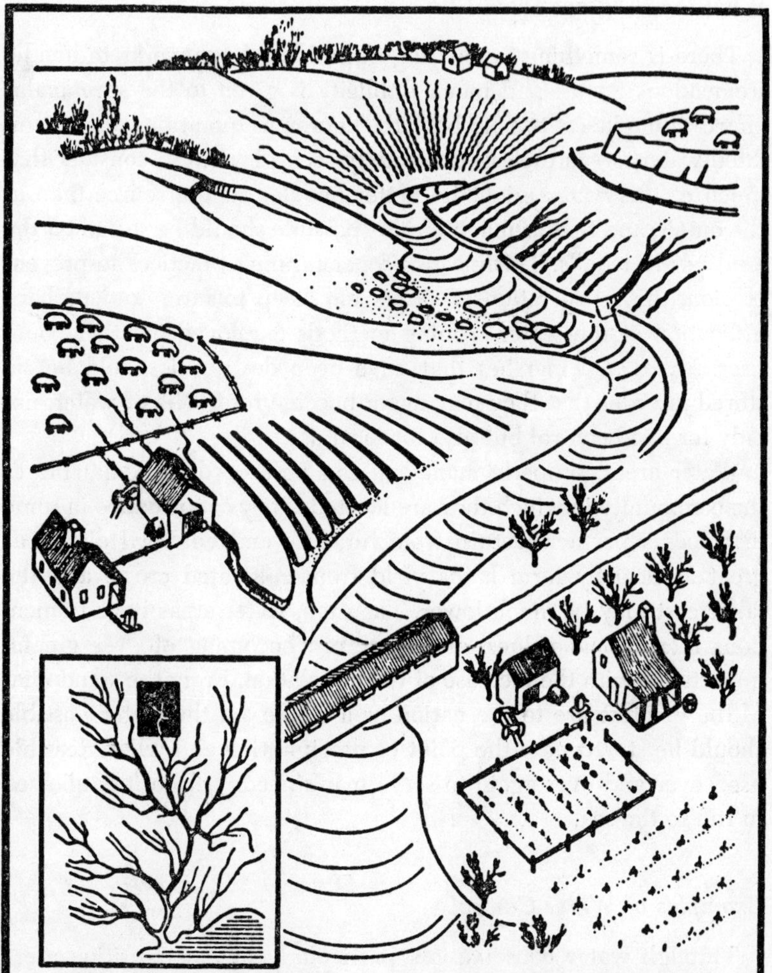

Fig. 4 / (From *Little Waters* by H. S. Person, et al., 1935.)

What the Program Should Be

There is something fascinating in building huge works to handle tremendous floods, and much publicity is given to the spectacular efforts of engineers to hold back the enormous quantities of accumulated water. Nevertheless, it certainly seems logical to consider that much of this water might be better handled at the source than at the outlet, and that as much of it as possible should be stored on the land where it falls. This means proper farming practices to prevent erosion, the revegetation of slopes too steep to farm, and perhaps utilization of the water-farming methods employed in other countries. Lakes and marshes that have been destroyed should be restored in order that they may again become reservoirs of water, not only for flood control but also for local use.

Water areas, properly managed, can be exceedingly valuable to the community in which they are located. They can produce in some instances a per acre return from fur, fish, and wildfowl almost as great as near-by farm lands yield from cultivated crops, and the labor cost may be much lower. Then too, water areas have tremendous recreational values, and these are becoming of ever greater importance with the increase of the population. From the standpoint of the greatest use to the nation as a whole, all the water possible should be stored near the point of precipitation and where feasible used over and over again to serve man's needs before it is allowed to run to the sea.

Examples of Water Control

Through water conservation, particularly in the transition areas between the wetter and the drier parts of the country, the total value of the land to the human population can be greatly increased. Much work along this line has been done in the past few years. Local, state, and Federal agencies have restored many ponds and lakes for various uses. Some were prepared to provide swimming and boating in communities where no surface water had been available. In June 1935, the State Game Commission made the statement that of 575 natural lakes in South Dakota only 5 held water enough to prevent their going dry in summer. This was due to drought and to the lowering of the water table by vast drainage operations over the preceding fifty years. Removal of the water destroyed also practically the entire muskrat population and disastrously reduced the fishes and waterfowl, natural assets of great value to the state. To overcome to some extent the difficulties created by drainage and drought, the state, with the aid of Federal funds, constructed several hundred dams to retain the spring run-off. Many of the dams are designed to maintain water at such depth that, regardless of lack of precipitation, it will not evaporate in any one season. These impoundments were stocked with fishes, which helped replace a source of fresh fish that was lost to the people of South Dakota by the destruction of their natural lakes. Such lakes again produce some fur animals and provide food for migratory waterfowl.

In North Dakota a great water-restoration and conservation program has been under way, and, among others things, this has helped restore water tables. Thus, many wells that formerly ran dry in summer again function the year round and some lands not now capable of producing any crop were benefited. In addition to raising the water tables and providing waterfowl refuges, for which many Federal impoundments in North Dakota were primarily undertaken, they serve to prevent floods in some of the river valleys. The Souris and James rivers are now so controlled by dams and other structures that it is doubtful whether their valleys will ever again be the scene of disastrous floods. The water-control structures on the Souris are estimated by engineers to be capable of handling, without any loss whatever, floods equal to all but three of the greatest that have ever been recorded in that basin. The Federal structures on the James River—in North Dakota at Jim and Arrowwood lakes, and in South Dakota at Sand Lake—together with others built by the states, should control with a minimum of damage any flood that may come down this watershed.

As water was accumulated, these areas produced an increasingly

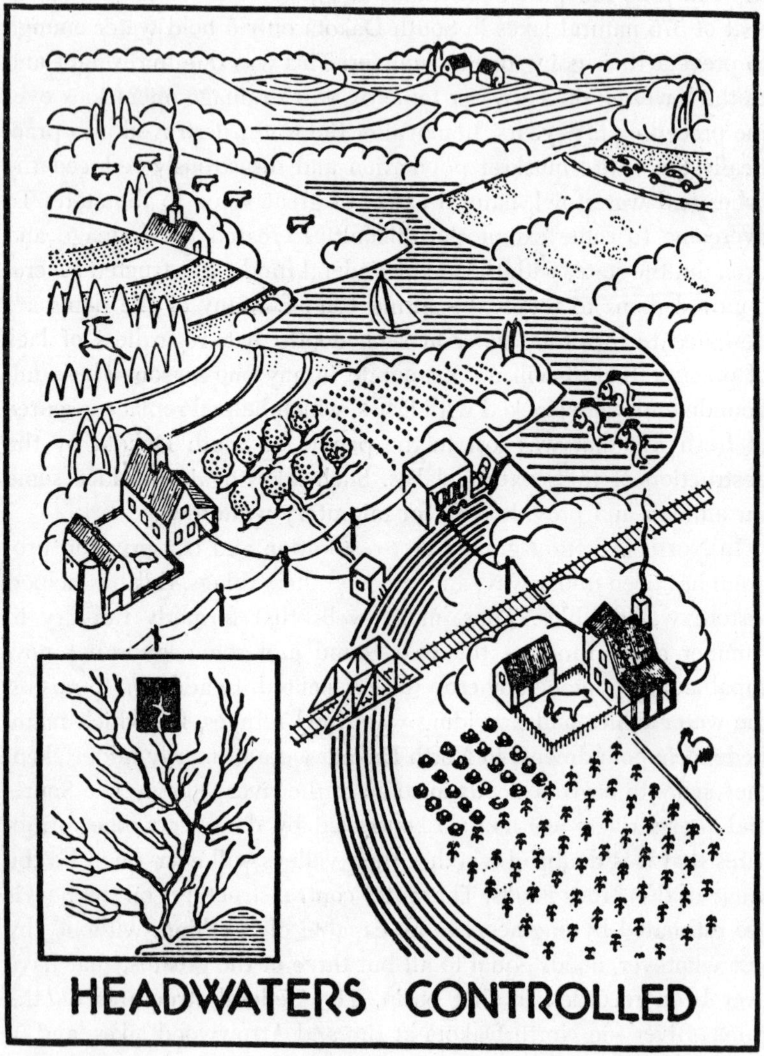

Fig. 5 / (From *Little Waters* by H. S. Person, et al., 1935.)

abundant crop of fur animals, as well as waterfowl and fishes, besides providing for a great deal of recreation. There is little question but that they are of more value to the community in their restored state than were their bottoms as farmlands. Such restoration is still going ahead not only in these states but in many others. However, drainage is still under way on an extensive scale even in areas that were searching desperately for water—any kind of water—during the dry 1930's.

To realize the highest use of water the national psychology with respect to it must undergo a change. The local promotion of extensive drainage projects, regardless of the effect upon the needs of the community as a whole and on the national economy, should be discouraged. Each project should be critically examined for its effect upon all uses, and the values of water carefully weighed against the proposed use. Unless it can be demonstrated that the project will result in greater permanent values it should not be undertaken.

Flood Control a National Problem

The problem of managing the waters of the basins of the Ohio, the Mississippi, and the other great river systems of the country should be regarded as of national scope. Properly handled these waters can be permanent national assets of the highest order, but improperly treated they can produce national catastrophes.

The Kansas City flood of July 1951 is a notable example. This flood crest exceeded all previous water stages on the Kansas River, caused much discussion, and already has been responsible for the expenditure of vast sums of money for flood control. Rendering more than a million people temporarily homeless and causing property damage to many millions of dollars, it furnished an impressive object lesson. For ten days before the flood, a stationary front poured rain on the Kansas River watershed—a downpour so abnormal as to cause a simultaneous rise of all its major tributaries. Such an extensive rainfall would have produced a flood even though every acre of the drainage basin had been covered with forests and other heavy vegetation. The flood crest, however, probably would not have reached such record height if so much of the land had not been lying open and fallow under intensive farming, riddled with tile ditches, crossed by open drains and straightened streams, and scalped smooth by the removal of brush and trees from the banks—all with the purpose of getting the surface water from the area in the shortest possible time. No one of these drains alone would have contributed much to the disaster, but multiplied a thousandfold their combined effect was to get rid of the run-off with a mighty rush of flood waters.

If flood-control programs on the Kansas River should result only in the building of great dams, levees, and dikes for the immediate protection of the great cities that were disastrously inundated, nothing will have been gained from the lesson the flood should have taught. The building of levees and dikes to confine rivers in their lower reaches without reduction in the total quantity of storm water that may quickly run into the valley is preparing the way for some later disaster of even greater proportions than any yet experienced. The great levee system on the lower Mississippi, while protecting many communities from floods, is in itself creating a problem that increases in gravity as time goes on. Confining this mighty stream to a narrow channel has been supposed to result in keeping the river bed scoured out. Actually the reverse has been the case: the bed of the river is building up so steadily that every few years it is necessary to raise the levees in order to prevent disaster to the cities and farms that lie behind them.

With all their faults, however, levees are necessary in the lowlands and will probably continue to be necessary for a long time, but the solution of flood problems will be found only in a national program that will begin to handle the waters at the point of precipitation.

Both small and large dams and levees, together with all other water-conservation practices, will be necessary if we are to obtain the best use of the water that falls on our lands. Skillful handling of water depends upon coördinating engineering and biological knowledge and upon land-use programs carefully worked out and applied to every major watershed where the need is evident.

The Solution Must Consider Wildlife

Every body of water, large or small, maintained to anywhere near a stabilized level, will produce aquatic vegetation and develop food for fishes and other wildlife. Every large dam built to stabilize water levels will add to the available food for fishes and waterfowl. Conversely, huge catch basins that are emptied entirely only to grow up to weeds and brush for several years before again being filled, are of little benefit to wildlife. In fact such basins will often result in a disaster that may be intensified if the catchment area fills during the bird-nesting season.

It seems not unreasonable to ask that at least some of the larger dams be built to create conservation pools at about the level the normal stream run-off will maintain. Temporary storage for excessive run-off could be provided above that level, the water to be drawn down to the normal lake level as soon as practicable without creating disastrous floods farther downstream. This would increase their value for wildlife, improve fish production, and preserve recreational values.

The welfare of migratory waterfowl, one of the great wildlife problems today, would be greatly promoted by the restoration or creation of innumerable bodies of water with levels nearly enough stabilized to permit the growth of food plants. Such a program would help diffuse the birds over areas not now occupied and tend to reduce the present great concentrations that not only are a menace to the birds themselves, but also produce complications in the way of damage to agricultural crops.

All in all, wildlife stands to gain much in any rational water-conservation program. The greatest danger that can be foreseen is that water conservation will be viewed entirely from the engineering standpoint, with no thought of other possible values to the nation through the concomitant safeguarding of the resource in wildlife that is dependent upon water and aquatic vegetation. Such a limited viewpoint would be a great misfortune in many ways. Much that can be done for wildlife and recreation should be undertaken in connection with flood control. If several purposes can be served it may justify expenditures that would not be warranted if only one of these objectives were being considered.

Type of Control Structure to Be Used

Whatever the type of flood-control structures, they should be designed by competent engineers and built adequately for their purpose. Much of the possible good from the development of small dams has been lost because of the fact that many of them were built without competent engineering supervision, only to go out with the first flood. Dams should be capable of standing up during the maximum floods, should be equipped with spillways that will handle all water in excess of the storage capacity, and should store water in ponds with sufficient depth, particularly in the more arid sections of the country, that one season of drought will not result in the disappearance of the water and the death of all the life dependent on it.

Adequate spillways are an essential part of any satisfactory dam structure, and water gates are desirable for use in flushing out the impoundage at least occasionally. The importance of providing for wildlife by the control of water levels in lakes and marshes should again be stressed. The less the fluctuation, the greater in general will be the wildlife values, although there are exceptions to the rule.

When large structures are necessary, it is not desirable to have dams of the type that create bodies of water that as summer progresses will shrink with great exposures of mud flats and shallow stagnant waters, particularly in seasons of subnormal rainfall. It is more desirable from the wildlife standpoint that several dams controlling water levels be constructed on the larger tributaries of a stream. Such lakes might well be created to utilize for maintenance the normal summer flow of the stream. Lakes so created will produce more wildlife and recreational values when they can be maintained with an uncompensated summer evaporation loss of a foot or less. When it becomes necessary to use the storage capacity above the normally maintained level there will inevitably be some loss of wildlife, but this is a risk that must be taken, considering the primary purpose of controlling flood waters and protecting property on the streams below. Even with such sporadic losses, however, the total average annual wildlife values on such areas will be much greater than if no consideration were given to wildlife needs in planning.

4 / Life of the Waters

The oceans, lakes, and streams, and even the small ponds and temporary pools, are not merely water—they contain also teeming communities of plant and animal life. All of these are adapted to their varied conditions and characterized by complicated interrelationships. Just as on the land, there is a cycle of life in the water, and there, also, plant life is its basis. A comparatively small part of the total vegetation of the waters is made up of higher plants. The diatoms, algæ, and other simpler forms, however, are abundant and perform the essential function of building a basic food supply for other kinds of life.

Aquatic Plant Life

Even the higher plants found in the waters are simple in structure compared with the familiar land plants. Many do not develop extensive feeding roots or even anchorage systems but obtain most of their nourishment directly from the water. Lacking also the stiffening woody structures found in trees, shrubs, and many other land plants, they are made up of more or less spongy tissues, which enable them to float free from the bottom to the height of their growth. Even during storms the plants are little disturbed, as the water of the oceans and lakes is calm a few feet below the surface. Their basic environment is comparatively stable, and normally its temperature varies but little. Aquatic plants, therefore, so long as the water remains, are not subjected to such great vicissitudes as are plants living on the land.

The only apparent exceptions are the marine plants that grow on the rocks between tide levels. These are usually algæ with tough rubbery stems and a foliage that allows them without harm to take the pounding of the waves. Being especially adapted to this hurly-burly, their colonies as a whole suffer little from storms.

Most of the more highly organized aquatic plants (the flowering types) grow in fresh water. They include the pondweeds, wild celery and allies, duckweeds, and other submerged, emergent, and floating plants. Some of these grow floating free on the surface while others, anchored on the bottom, may grow entirely covered with water or with their tops protruding above it. Among the simpler forms are the diatoms, some of which are free floating, some cover the surface of fixed objects, and others inhabit the bottom. Along with the diatoms grow algæ of various degrees of complexity, all the way from one- or few-celled kinds to the giant kelp, which may be several hundred or even a thousand feet in length. All carry on the process of photosynthesis, which is necessary to their own and other life, and all perform the further important function of releasing oxygen in the water, thus helping to maintain its oxygen content, which is so necessary to the existence of the higher forms of animal life.

The Life Cycle in the Water

The life cycle, somewhat simplified in both fresh and salt water, is essentially the same as on the land. As the algæ die, their decaying bodies, broken down by bacteria, release into the waters the organic compounds that were built by their own life processes and will be absorbed directly by a new growth of similar plants. Or these simple plants may be consumed by microscopic animals, and these in turn by small crustaceans or tiny fishes, which, fulfilling their part in the food chain, become prey for the larger carnivorous fishes, sharks, porpoises, and seals, or of the birds that feed on or near the surface.

The greatly varied interrelationships between the organisms make the cycle infinitely complex, but the essential features follow the familiar pattern. Plants collect the mineral elements found in the water in minute quantities and build them into their own structures in combination with the carbohydrates that they manufacture in sunlight from elements taken from the water. The plants may then either be eaten or be returned to the water by decay. Eventually all or nearly all the plant-synthesized matter is returned to the water, thus maintaining the basic food supply for organisms in general. Nowhere has this cycle been expressed more forcefully than by Murphy, in his *Oceanic Birds of South America* (vol. 1, pp. 61-62),* as follows:

"The organic source of all food in the sea, for creatures of the depths as well as those of the surface layer and of the air above, is the microscopic plant life, comprising most of the diatoms and brown algæ which, obtaining their sustenance directly from the nutrient ions in the circulation, build up tissue that becomes the food of small crustaceans, certain fishes, etc., which, in their turn, are devoured by birds and other higher animals.

" 'The sun's rays penetrate into the upper layers of the water; oxygen and carbon dioxide are dissolved from the atmosphere and mineral salts are brought in from the land by rivers. These are ideal conditions for plant life; the sea is one great culture medium. Just as the agents favoring life are scattered through the medium, so is life itself; it is scattered as a fine aquatic dust of microscopic single-celled plants in untold billions (Hardy, 1928, 211).'

"In the presence of sunlight the microscopic plants assimilate the carbon of carbonic acid and restore oxygen to solution, thus bettering the conditions for animal life. Under optimum circumstances, these plant forms may number tens, or even hundreds, of thousands per liter of ocean water. They exist principally in a stratum within a hundred meters of the

* Murphy, Robert Cushman. *Oceanic Birds of South America: A Study of Species of the Related Coasts and Seas, including the American Quadrant of Antarctica, Based upon the Brewster-Sanford Collection in the American Museum of Natural History*. 2 vols., illus., New York, 1936.

surface, though they sometimes penetrate three or four times as far, and their dead remains are uninterruptedly settling into the lightless depths. But so-called 'vertical' circulation, in which as a rule, the angle of ascent is probably very slight, in many parts of the ocean returns masses of deeper water to the surface and thereby prevents food substances in the form of decomposition products from accumulating out of reach of the photosynthetic plant zone. This means that while water denuded of some of its chemical nutrients is carried down, other masses of water that have been enriched during their sojourn below are being restored to the surface. Here, if the food material is not directly available to the algæ, it may be utilized by bacteria and worked over into substances which enable the profuse development of other plant life to go on.

"Harvey (1928, 165) calls attention to the important fact that, in addition to a supply of phytoplankton suitably spaced in time, a further condition necessary for maximum population is that the energy of plant life passed on to the plankton-feeding animals must, before the latter die, be handed in turn to carnivorous animals; therefore it cannot be assumed that where vegetable, carbohydrate, and protein food exists there will necessarily be an animal population to eat a fixed proportion of it. In the case of simple death of a phytoplankton cell, writes Allen (1934, 178), it may be supposed that decomposition by bacteria or other saprophytic forms brings derivatives from the body substance to a soluble or suspended condition in the surrounding water, from which some of them may be removed by another cell for its own use. For some particular atom it may be possible for the circuit to be very short, *i.e.* diatom—bacterium—sea water—diatom. In most cases it is longer as: diatom—copepod—herring—cod (or bird)—bacterium—sea water—diatom. Long or short, there is no room for doubt that photosynthetic organisms occupy the key position in the food exchange of the ocean. Harvey's diagram* of the closed circuit is as follows:

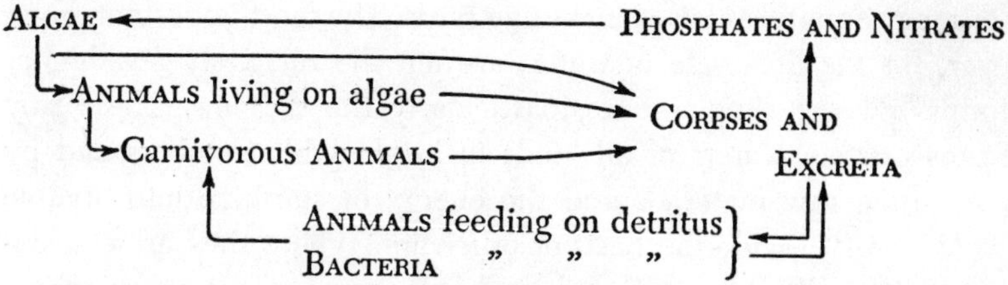

* This diagram is used by permission of the Cambridge University Press, publishers of H. W. Harvey's *The Biological Chemistry and Physics of Sea Water* (1928), in which it was first published.

" 'This schema shows that the fertility of an ocean will depend for the most part upon two factors, namely the length of time taken by the corpses of marine organisms and excreta to decay, and the length of time taken by the phosphates and nitrates so formed to come again within the range of algal growth. Where the corpses fall in deep water, well below the light intensity necessary for photosynthesis, and where there is no vertical mixing of the water or deep currents to take the phosphates and nitrates to lesser depths, they are likely to remain lost for many years to the cycle of life owing to the long period which must elapse after the salts are reformed from dead organisms and before they again reach the upper sunlit layers. The process of decay will be slower in the cold bottom water of a deep ocean than in the comparatively warm bottom water of shallow areas. In most places it is the time taken for the re-formed salts to be transported to the upper layers which will predominate, rather than the length of time taken by the dead organisms to decay (Harvey, 1928, 168)'.

"In this causal sequence the diatoms are the connecting link between the energy of the sun and the oceanic animal world, including birds. The diatoms surpass in bulk or annual productiveness all other aquatic plants a thousandfold. They are the pasture of the sea; they are highly nutritious and there are perhaps no deleterious species. They are everywhere available, though most so in ocean waters of relatively low temperature, and because of their abundance they represent the sole food supply of certain marine animals, the partial sustenance of many more, and the ultimate source of life for all."

Food Value of Aquatic Plants

All water plants are important direct or indirect sources of food for many aquatic animals, including birds. The most important, however, for the life cycle in water, are not the relatively few higher forms but the simpler ones, particularly the diatoms. These tiny forms exist in waters of all kinds in incalculable numbers and by combining raw materials and the energy of sunshine into organic compounds provide the basis of other life. Where they are concentrated other life also is abundant, but in areas of the ocean where they are scarce, there are few of the higher forms of life.

Aquatic plants provide little human food, although in the Orient, particularly in China, some of the kelps, arrowheads, and spike-rushes are utilized to a certain extent. The roots and seeds of certain aquatics were eaten at times by the American Indians. Among these may be mentioned the wapato and chufa, the tubers of which were eagerly sought. The seeds of smartweeds were sometimes gathered and ground into a meal that could be used in cooking. Today, with the exception of wild rice, which is an important food for Wisconsin and Minnesota Indians, and is also sold by them, water plants of this country make little direct contribution to the food of the human race. They do, however, make possible an abundance of fishes, fur-bearing animals, and aquatic birds, all of which are important to man.

Factors Affecting Plants of Inland Waters

Among factors affecting the abundance of plant life in inland waters are the rapidity of stream flow, the fluctuation of water levels in either lakes or streams, and the amount of sediment or pollution carried in the waters. The last named may affect plants in two ways, one by obscuring the sunlight and thus interfering with photosynthesis, and the other by actually burying the plants. The type of soil in the bottom has a great influence on plants in inland waters, and the chemical content of the water a still greater influence. There are plants that can exist only in salt water, some that prefer brackish, and others that can survive only in fresh water. The lime content of the water sometimes makes a vast difference in the quantity of its aquatic vegetation. The chemical composition of the water being so important, it is not surprising that when industrial wastes in the form of sulfuric acid or similar noxious substances are added, plant life is destroyed, sometimes for many miles below the source of pollution.

While a moderate quantity of domestic sewage might enrich the waters and produce more plant growth, gross pollution has a fatal effect, and our streams become nothing more than sewers. A stream might assimilate a certain amount of sewage but beyond that point its oxygen content is used in oxidizing the sewage to an extent that renders it unfit for fishes or other aquatic animals.

Pollution has come about primarily because it is easier for industrial plants and cities to dump their wastes and sewage into streams and lakes than to dispose of them in some less destructive way. Many industries, of far less value to the welfare of this country than the resources they destroy, continually publicize the fact that they could not be operated at a profit if they had to install modern methods of waste disposal. From the standpoint of the individual owner this is important, but from that of the public it would seem far better in the long run to protect the productivity of the waters of the country than to permit individuals to profit from operations that destroy this productivity. The problem is far more weighty than mere conservation of water: it goes to the roots of the question of whether we shall so handle the resources of the nation that they will increase in value rather than continue to decline as they have in the past hundred years.

Fishes

The originally unpolluted waters, with abundant aquatic plant life, were very favorable for fishes. Since the settlement of the country by the white man, however, the situation has been greatly changed. Many of the lakes and ponds have been drained; dams have been built that prevent the runs of migratory fishes from reaching the spawning grounds; streams have been straightened and deepened until the sluggish pools that formerly harbored plant growth are no more; and pollution has often destroyed all aquatic life. Many streams, which a comparatively few years ago produced an abundance of fishes and other life of value to the human race, are now barren. The Atlantic salmon has been exterminated in the coastal streams south of Maine and continues to exist only in a few rivers in that state. The shad run is gone or has decreased tremendously in most of the streams that formerly produced this delicious food fish. Sturgeons are now rare in the Mississippi Valley. The

Great Lakes fisheries, once offering the most valuable freshwater fishes on the continent, now have only a fraction of their former value. Overfishing has played a part in all these decreases, particularly in the Great Lakes, but the waters have often been spoiled to such an extent that under present conditions the restoration of the fishes is impossible.

Fundamentally this destruction of a valuable food resource has occurred because of man's failure to comprehend its value and to appreciate the necessity of proper management. Fishes, like all other forms of life, require food and shelter throughout the year if they are to reproduce themselves and provide continuing harvestable crops. Since water is a less familiar living medium to man than the air in which he normally lives, there is even less popular understanding of the needs of aquatic animals than there is of the species that inhabit the land.

Fishes are of many types. Some feed upon plants and plant products, some on insects, crustaceans, mollusks, and other small life of the waters, while others are predatory on smaller fishes or are even cannibalistic. Many require special environmental conditions; others are exceedingly adaptable and can live and thrive under astonishingly dissimilar conditions. Some are valued as a commercial source of food only; many provide sport and recreation as well as food; and still others are of importance from the human standpoint because they yield products valuable in the arts and industries or are food for better fishes. All need a year-round supply of food, suitable spawning areas, and cover for protection from enemies.

Cover varies for different types, but for many of the more valuable fishes a vigorous growth of aquatic plants is necessary to provide shelter for the young and also to provide homes for the minute forms of animal life on which they feed.

There is great interest in the game fishes, and large sums of money have been spent trying to maintain sport fishing in the face of a decreasing area of suitable waters. Several hundred fish hatcheries—where young sport fishes are grown artificially—are in operation at the present time, producing stock for planting in waters where fish populations are depleted. All too often these efforts have been nonproductive because fry have been planted in waters deficient either in food or in suitable environment for them. Now there is a growing tendency to try to improve or restore conditions in streams and lakes so as to enable fishes again to reproduce naturally in waters that at present are nonproductive, or, if that is not possible, to give fishes a chance to survive by planting them only in waters that are suited to their requirements.

Fish management is not different basically from quail or deer management. The three fundamentals are: (1) to provide suitable environment, (2) to limit the harvest to the crop produced, and (3) to keep populations in balance with the food supply. The management of fish differs from that of warm-blooded animals in that when deer or rabbits become overly abundant, the reproduction rate is lowered, and mortality, particularly in the younger age classes, increases; when fish become overly abundant, the reproductive rate remains high but growth of individuals ceases. The result is a stunted population of little interest to the angler.

Regulating the harvest is already under way. Although there has been a general trend toward liberalization of fishing restrictions, in recent years, many states have laws fixing seasons or otherwise limiting the catch. Where such regulations are needed, particularly with regard to the salmonids and other cold-water fish, restrictions should be stringent enough to leave sufficient breeding stocks.

Studies in recent years have revealed a more complete understanding of the population dynamics of warm-water fishes. It was previously thought that overfishing was the major cause of the deterioration of sport fisheries in lakes and ponds. Biologists, however, now recognize that the differential in breeding potential between the highly prolific panfish and the less prolific but more desirable large game fish is a major factor. Although the game fish are predatory by nature, the tiny fry of both groups compete directly with one another for food. Eventually, the coarse species or panfish predominate because of their greater numbers. Unwise stocking programs and well-meaning habitat restoration programs that favored the less desirable species have contributed to this problem in the past. Population controls are now widely used and take the form of partial or complete removal of all fish through selective poisoning and the restocking of the waters with balanced populations, liberalized fishing seasons to encourage the removal of less desirable species, and destruction of spawning beds of panfish.

Along with this movement has been a growing practice of providing improvement in environments for fish life. This has brought fish conservationists in contact with some of the fundamental general conservation problems, including those relating to soil erosion, drainage, and water pollution. Two very necessary prerequisites to providing favorable conditions for an abundant fish life are the abatement of pollution and the prevention of excessive sedimentation—in other words, soil conservation. Lakes or ponds that have been drained likewise must be restored before they can be usable for fishes, and therefore drainage is a destructive factor for fish life as well as other forms. Given water to work with, there are available to skilled fish technicians devices that can improve conditions for fish populations just as there are similar techniques in the field of game bird and animal management.

Some of the methods used in restoring streams to greater productiveness of fishes and fish foods may be mentioned. Logs and trees felled into the water—and fastened in place where necessary—help in creating favorable pools. Stone or log dams or weirs often help serve the same purpose if provision is made for fishes to move up and down stream over these obstructions. Building fish ladders over larger dams is vitally necessary in streams that support runs of migratory fishes, such as the salmons of the West. Control of water levels in lakes and ponds is important generally, and in the drier areas the water should be deep enough to protect the entire body of water and its included fish life from destruction by evaporation. This point should also be carefully studied in any program of reflooding drained lakes or marshes.

The steady decline of fresh-water commercial fisheries over a long period of time has been due in part to some one or more of the factors mentioned above, and in many instances to overexploitation of remaining stocks already declining under adverse conditions. The same may be said of the fishing in salt and brackish water bays and in the streams emptying into them. Such varied and useful forms as crabs, oysters, shrimps, and scallops, and the marine fishes that enter brackish or fresh water to spawn, have declined woefully under a combination of overexploitation, pollution, and silting of spawning beds or blocking access to them by huge dams, until they have only a fraction of their former value. The restoration of these fisheries, once the source of a wholesome supply of food and also the basis of livelihood for many thousands of families, is just as dependent upon a wise solution of the problem of water conservation and wise use as in the case of the inland and fresh-water fisheries.

Oceanic fisheries are not, at present, involved in many of these problems that harass the inland fisheries. There is, however, one wise precaution that should always be kept in mind—that is keeping the harvest in proper relation to reproduction.

Fur Animals

Aquatic environments once produced an abundance of fur-bearing animals. In fact, some of the most valuable fur animals of the continent are intimately associated with water. These include the beaver, the otter, the mink, and the muskrat. Although many extensive marshes once used by muskrats have been destroyed by drainage, this animal still remains our most important fur producer. Beavers and otters were reduced by overtrapping rather than by pollution, but in recent years restocking and management programs have greatly improved the status of the beaver. Minks also have been reduced by overtrapping, but they have been handicapped also by the destruction of their food supplies by pollution. In these four animals we have the basis of an industry that once was a great national asset, and one that under proper management of the waters could again become a much more valuable natural resource.

Water Birds

The conservation of water is intimately associated also with the fate of the migratory waterfowl, the ducks, geese, and swans, as well as of many other marsh-inhabiting birds, including coots, rails, shorebirds, and many species not classed as game. All these fill a place in the natural scheme, and their existence depends on the condition of the waters.

Both fur animals and migratory waterfowl are discussed more fully elsewhere in this book and are mentioned here only to indicate the ramifications of the water-conservation problem.

Water Management

Inland, unless a restoration of water productivity is undertaken on a large scale, this country may become more or less dependent on pond culture for its food fishes. In fact there is already a small industry now in operation that supplies artificially reared trout, bass, perch, carp, and similar fishes, for local markets and a small fish farming industry in connection with rice growing in the South. There may, therefore, be a lesson to be found in the upper Rhone Valley in France. The following quotation from the volume *Little Waters* (pp. 65-67)* outlines briefly the practice employed there in handling water and land jointly:

". . . Its characteristics are in major respects similar to those of the Upper Mississippi Valley—hills and stretches of moderate gradient; fertile soils intermixed with rocks, pebbles, gravel, sand, and clay; and streams winding among the hills and over the gently sloping areas.

"French farming is noted for its efficiency. It is based on the principle

* Person, H. S., Coil, E. J., and Beall, R. T. *Little Waters: A Study of Headwater Streams and Other Little Waters, Their Uses and Relations to the Land.* 82 pp., illus., Washington, Government Printing Office, 1935 [rev. 1936].

of working with Nature; of adapting the crops to the land, rather than attempting to adapt the land to crops, and of utilization of all factors of soil and water—physical, chemical, and biological. With respect to some of these factors neighboring farmers coöperate, as in the use of waters. . . . The Upper Rhone Valley is dotted with ponds, most of them man-made. The location of these ponds is shifted from year to year, in accordance with each farmer's rotation of 'land farming' with 'water farming,' based on coöperative arrangements respecting the use of waters.

"These temporary ponds may vary from a few acres to six or seven hundred acres. The most satisfactory location is a slightly depressed, typical grain field. This area can if necessary be surrounded by an earth dike to insure the size and depth needed to capture and retain the usual run-off. The depth, which varies with the danger from ice, the local rate of evaporation, and with the amount of rainfall or stream water which may be expected to replace the evaporation, is usually not less than 4 feet.

"The rotation of use of such a site, variable to meet market and other conditions, is generally as follows: 1 or 2 years of water crop (fish and fowl) alternating with 1 year of grain (wheat or barley). Each crop prepares and improves the soil for the next. This treatment may in places and on occasion be supplemented by small quantities of lime and potash (wood ashes) or phosphate (rock or acid) and nitrates (protein waste from house and barn) to correct accidental deficiencies.

"The biological principle involved is that the stubble of grain, the cellulose material and dead leaves and twigs when under water are attacked and eaten by fungi, notably bacteria. Floating in the atmosphere and resting in the soil and other material are dried bodies of plants mingled with which are forms of animal life—infusoria. These and similar organisms become activated in the presence of water, if it is correct in quantity and quality. The end result is aquatic vegetation that is food for fish and fowl, the farmer's water crop. After the pond is drained in the rotation plan, the aquatic vegetation is greedily pastured by the farm animals, while the protein material left behind, including the unutilized bodies of fishes and aquatic animals, becomes transformed into manure for the following grain crop. Because of the regulated biological action incident to the rotation, these ponds are generally free from malaria.

"Under favorable natural conditions generally, equal areas yield comparable profits from both land and water farming, and thus are reduced the natural hazards in farm practice."

A similar type, as well as other types of fish farming, has long been practiced in the Orient.

It should be evident that certain fundamentals must be observed if the wildlife of the waters is to be restored to its real usefulness. These may be summarized briefly as follows:

1. New pollution of streams and lakes must not be permitted, and existing sources of pollution must be removed as rapidly as possible.
2. Soil-erosion control goes hand in hand with this program. The prevention of silting is often a vital necessity to making the rivers again productive.
3. Flood-control programs can and should be so designed as to help restore aquatic life rather than further to handicap it.
4. Making small impoundments on the headwaters of tributaries should become a widespread practice.
5. Lakes and marshes now drained should be restored whenever possible.
6. Drainage of additional lakes and marshes and stream straightening should be discouraged.
7. Management of fishes, fur animals, and other products of water areas should be on the crop basis, with the preservation of breeding stocks a matter of first concern.
8. Water should take its rightful place in popular thought. It should be treated and handled as a valuable resource rather than as an enemy.

5 / Forest Conservation

When the white man came to America he found one of the greatest forests that ever existed. Upwards of 820,000,000 acres of the continental United States, or somewhat less than half the total land surface, was covered by trees. The wooded area extended in an almost unbroken stand from the Atlantic to the Mississippi. Beyond that river forests grew over southern Missouri, all of Arkansas and Louisiana, and the eastern parts of Oklahoma, Texas, and Iowa, and most of Minnesota. The far western forests occupied mountain slopes generally of the Rocky Mountain states and the Great Basin, and covered approximately the western half of Oregon and Washington and northern California, with the exception of the Sacramento Valley.

In the East much of the original forest was laid waste in the land-clearing operations. The present great farm belt east of the Mississippi originally was largely forested land. According to the latest estimates, about 630,000,000 acres, or a little less than four-fifths of the original wooded area of the continental United States, except Alaska, is still worth more for forest production than it is for cultivated crops or any other purpose.

The concept on which the forest restoration and conservation program in this country is based is that forests and their products are useful and valuable to the human race in many ways; and that it is the part of wisdom to grow forests on all suitable lands not needed for some other purpose.

Importance of Forests

As pointed out in a previous chapter, plant growth, including forests, plays an important part in the life cycle. Plants are the soil builders and the true creators of food that can be passed indirectly from one plant to another or directly from plant to animal form, perhaps through several animals in succession, and finally back to the soil. In addition to being a factor in building soil, forests are of value also in regulating stream flow and controlling erosion and in providing cover and food for various wild animals, grazing for domestic herds, and commodities and recreation for man. Many of our denuded forest areas are now coming back into timber by natural reproduction. Some of the lands are so badly eroded, however, that artifical planting and a long and slow process of soil building must take place before they can again produce their former volume of forest products. By intelligent use, all the forest resources can be maintained and at the same time utilized for the benefit of the human race.

The ownership of forest lands in this country, according to the latest reports, is divided about as follows:

PRESENT OWNERSHIP AND ACREAGE OF FOREST LANDS

Ownership	*Noncommercial*	*Commercial*	*Total*
Private	58,500,000	358,300,000	416,800,000
Public	117,100,000	130,300,000	247,400,000
Total	175,600,000	488,600,000	664,200,000

Of the 358,000,000 acres of private commercial forest lands, about 165,000,000 acres are owned by some 3,400,000 farmers, and about 193,000,000 acres are held by about a million industrial and nonfarm operators.

Public ownership of commercial forest lands breaks down about as follows:

Ownership	*Acres*
Community	8,000,000
State	20,000,000
Federal Indian Reservations	7,000,000
National Forests	85,000,000
Public Domain	6,000,000
Other Federal	5,000,000
Total	131,000,000

On these areas of forest, management varies in degree, from the highest to the simplest or none at all. Most individual timberland owners still see the forest as only a certain number of saw logs that must be cut and marketed within the shortest possible space of time. These owners are not entirely to blame, for antiquated local taxation policies, heavy costs of protecting forests from fire, insects, or disease, marketing difficulties, and other problems often force them either to cut and market the timber speedily or to go into bankruptcy. On the Federal and on some state forests a high degree of forest management is practiced, and the administrative policies in handling these forests are far removed from the policy of quick liquidation.

While forests have been, and will continue to be, of great value for timber, many people have come to the conclusion that their other values and certain services that forests perform may be worth more than the returns from timber alone. Like the agricultural lands that must continue to grow the cultivated crops on which the nation depends, commercial forest lands also can serve as a permanent source of livelihood for the human race. As products of soil fertility and precipitation, they are capable of furnishing more employment than an equal area of grasslands, which rank next in the general land-use classification.

Two main principles to be observed in modern forest practice are multiple use and sustained-yield harvesting. Both fit into the general conservation program and their demonstrated importance has greater weight than any single concept of forest values.

Multiple-Use Principle in Forest Management

The multiple-use concept, laid down more than 50 years ago as basic principle in national forest administration, is that all uses of forested lands shall be considered and that they shall be so correlated that the greatest public benefit will result. In some cases, however, when a certain use is found to be of first importance, others must be subordinated to it. For example, near a large center of population, when no other facilities for outdoor recreation are available, a forest might easily be more valuable for public recreation than for any or all other possible uses combined. But use of forest lands for two or more purposes is generally possible through sensible adjustment or compromise. This is the philosophy of administration of the national forests and of many that are under state control.

The main uses to which timberlands may be put vary in importance with the region, the type of forest, and the economic conditions of the area in which the forest is situated. In addition to improving and protecting the forests, forest reservations were originally established "for the purpose of securing favorable conditions of waterflow and to furnish a continuous supply of timber for the use and necessity of citizens of the United States." (Act of June 4, 1897.)

The concept of forest uses has expanded, but timber production is still one of the major forest values. Better forest management promises a steady supply of wood products that may vary all the way from saw logs and pulpwood to charcoal, turpentine, maple syrup and sugar, tanbark, cascara bark, sumac, nuts, blueberries and other wild fruits, and ornamental plants. In addition to these the forests produce many wild roots and plants formerly much used by the Indians and still consumed to some extent by both Indians and their white neighbors. These include bulbs such as those of

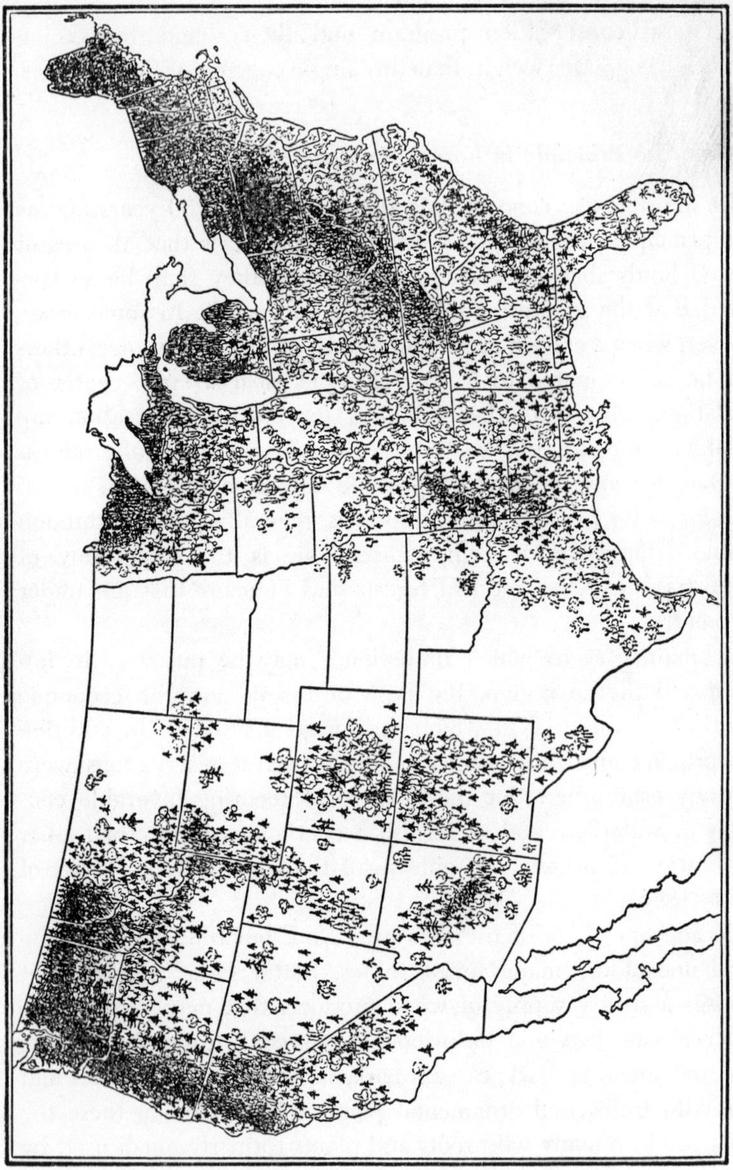

Fig. 6 / Forest areas of the United States.
(By U. S. Forest Service.)

camass and erythronium, rice roots and other succulent roots of many kinds, plants for holiday decorations, packing, and surgical dressing, and many other products. Locally some of these are very important. Maple products are of tremendous value to communities in the northeastern states. The peeling of cascara bark on the Pacific coast furnishes spring employment and a cash income to many families. At blueberry-picking time in some of the western mountains, tent cities of hundreds of people spring up where the plants are producing a good crop, and other wild berries are similarly harvested. Many kinds of nuts are gathered from forests throughout the land, and the harvesting of greens for Christmas decoration furnishes employment for many people. There is an extensive industry in the Carolina mountains in selecting, gathering, and shipping rhododendrons, azaleas, and other plants that propagate rapidly there. All these are by-products of only local importance, but the aggregate income received from them is of vast importance to nearby communities.

Grazing Use of Forests

On some of the forest lands, particularly in the western states, the agricultural areas are often limited to those that can be irrigated, and therefore the livestock industry makes grazing another highly important forest use. More than 4,000,000 cattle and sheep use national forests for grazing in summer, while most of them are carried through the winter by the hay and other feeds produced on the agricultural lands.

Though grazing on forest and other lands has in the past been overdone, there is no reason why it cannot be regulated in the public interest. Grazing should be so restricted and controlled that the vegetative cover will not be destroyed, as this results in excessive run-off, with consequent soil erosion and destruction of the range. In some parts of the southern states, wooded lands have been so overrun with hogs and other livestock that considerable damage has been done to the forest and forest reproduction is prevented. There are many forest areas that should not be grazed at all, some that can be grazed lightly, and others that can provide considerable quantities of feed regularly if properly handled by skilled range managers.

Range-deterioration problems can be worked out locally by properly trained individuals, and where forest lands have been put under intensive management there has been a gradual improvement in the vegetative cover and in grazing conditions. Sometimes, as during the 1930's, drought has interfered materially with the carrying out of corrective programs for the range, and emergency needs and uses that require local adjustment to prevent human suffering have interfered with the upbuilding of the range and the restoration of other natural resources. Normally, however, it should be the general policy to hold grazing somewhat below the carrying capacity of the range, in order to restore vegetative covers that have been depleted, to aid in their maintenance after they are restored, and to build up a reserve. If these principles are followed the grasslands and open forest lands of the western states should provide a permanent source of wealth to the American people without serious harm to forest and other values.

Forests as Soil and Water Conservators

As has been noted, the presence of vegetative cover means that the soil is building up, and forests are great and useful soil builders. The dead leaves, fallen branches, and other litter gradually rot and, in returning to the soil, form a porous humus. As this mixes with the mineral constituents of the soil, it increases its water-absorbing capacity and its ability to retard the run-off. Where the surface is protected the masses of living roots and rootlets of the trees also help hold the soil in place. All the leaves, twigs, dying parts of the trees, and the trees themselves that have fallen, mingled with the litter from shrub and other growth in the forest, gradually build up a high humus content, making the soil richer from year to year and capable of producing more and better forest growth.

The forests are valuable also in direct watershed protection. An abundant supply of water, including drinking water, is essential to all life, including man. Many cities are favorably situated for having their sources of water supply in forest lands. In such cases the forests are often administered primarily for watershed protection, this sometimes excluding any other use. This exclusion may be temporary or it may be permanent, depending on local conditions.

In helping regulate the run-off, forests also play an important part in water conservation. The great absorptive capacity of humus and litter on the forest floor and the retarding effect of shade on the melting of snow both operate to extend the time of the run-off. Under this natural regulation, the streams run less water during flood crests and continue a more sustained flow in summer than would otherwise be the case. This agency of the forests does not obviate the great floods that are the result of a precipitation so heavy over wide areas as to exceed the capacity of the soil to absorb or retain. Forest cover does, however, help in holding down the crests of these floods and so to lessen their destructiveness.

F. A. Silcox, former Chief of the Forest Service, has given some interesting illustrations of forest values in retarding the run-off:

"Pickens and San Dimas and Frankish, mountain canyons opening into fertile southern California valleys, are apt illustrations. Fire removed forest cover on 5,000 acres in Pickens Canyon in 1933, but did not visit San Dimas Canyon. Late in December of that year, a heavy storm hit both these canyons alike. A few days later, a flood swept out of Pickens Canyon, destroyed 200 homes and killed thirty-four persons. There was no flood from unburned San Dimas Canyon. In 1935, fire swept nearby Frankish Canyon. Early in 1936, floods swept out of it through the city of Upland. The same storm struck unburned San Dimas Canyon. With forest cover intact there was no flood; San Dimas waters continued clear.

"The Forest Service had rain gauges and other controls in all three of these California canyons. Measurements in other parts of the country afford similar information. Just before the 1936 flood on one of the tributaries of the Susquehanna, nine-tenths of the rain falling on a potato field was lost as run-off, and carried with it more than 1,000 pounds of soil from every acre. But in the same storm a neighboring forested area lost only one-half of one per cent of the precipitation, and no soil."*

Other studies have been under way since 1934 in the southern Appalachian Mountains of South Carolina at the Coweeta Experiment Forest. Here, numerous nearly identical drainage areas have been studied thoroughly and then treated by different methods to determine the effects of forests and forest management on water run-off. They have shown conclusively that grazing, cultivation of steep slopes, and improper logging practices have serious detrimental effects on both soil and water yields in mountain hardwood forests.

Recreation Afforded by Forests

The recreational use of the forest has come prominently to public attention in the past few years. Expressed in the number of visitors to national forests, this use increased the visits from about 3,000,000 persons in 1916 to more than 52,500,000 in 1956. Recreation is now a major forest land use, both in the East and in much of the West. In most national forests, however, there is room for other uses without seriously interfering with their enjoyment by the people who reside in the vicinity or by those who come from a distance. Recognition of the increasing public benefits to be derived from the recreational uses of the forests will give added weight to the growing sentiment in favor of forest conservation.

Wildlife Denizens

In the multiple-use plan for forests, the preservation of stocks of wildlife, both game and nongame species, is recognized as of major importance. Forests that are not too dense are the natural home of many important small species of mammals and of birds and big game. Not only do the moose, deer, and elk now find their

* Silcox, F. A. *A New Policy for Flood Control.* American Forests, vol. 43, no. 3, pp. 106-108, 146-147, illus. March 1937.

most suitable habitat in forested lands, but also some of the larger carnivores, including the bear, wolf, mountain lion, and bobcat. Among the game birds of the woodland are the wild turkey, blue and ruffed grouse, and mountain quail; and among the valuable fur-bearing animals are the beaver, fisher, marten and wolverine. There are, of course, a great many smaller forms of both birds and mammals in the forests. Most of our valuable trout streams lie in timbered regions, and the condition of these streams and the method of handling them will determine to a large extent the recreational angling that will be available to the people.

A separate chapter is devoted to the relationships between forestry and wildlife; hence it is enough here to say that many animals can survive only in forests and that their existence depends upon the consideration that is given them in forest management.

Sustained-Yield Forest Management

The second major premise of forestry practice so important in any modern conservation program is that of sustained yield. Sustained-yield forest management is attained only (a) when usable growing timber arrives at the age and condition for cutting as fast as timber is removed by cutting and through fire and other causes; and (b) when it arrives in such volume that dependent industries can operate and dependent labor can work continuously. This is now a governing principle on national forests, some state forests, and on a small but increasing proportion of the forest land in private ownership. Included in the last category are those properties in the Tree Farm Program, which is designed to promote the growing and harvesting of trees as a permanent business.

The plan may be called continuous annual cropping. The timber available from a convenient mill site is studied to determine the annual increment, and a cutting cycle is set up, based on the average number of years that it will take to grow a timber crop in the locality. Upon the basis of the timber available, the rate of cutting is fixed, so that the total area tributary to the mill will be cut over in the normal period needed for growth of timber of merchantable size. This may be thirty years or more, depending on the type of timber, the fertility of the soil, the rainfall, and other factors.

This method is in great contrast to that in more general use, which may well be called the "cut-and-get-out" system. In early days men cut off the forests of the Lake States and moved on, leaving behind them a devastated country, towns without hope of future employment for their citizens, and generally bankrupt communities. The same practice was employed in the South also, and it has made its appearance in the last remaining virgin forests of the West. Some of the original eastern hardwood forests were treated even worse. In many cases they were not logged at all—the trees were simply girdled and killed in order to make room for agricultural crops, or they were felled and piled in fields to be burned or left to rot. Where they were logged, it was by the favorite ruinously exploitative system.

The sustained-yield concept, by replacing exploitation, is designed to benefit the communities affected. It looks toward the permanent maintenance of populations around the mills, with a steady source of employment and income. In other words, stabilization both of communities and of community values is to replace the abrupt changes that prevailed in connection with the lumber operations of the past. Even though the cutting of the last great timber stands in Oregon and Washington is still under way, ghost towns are already found and more are being created. From both a local and a national standpoint it would be much better to harvest the timber gradually, so that the towns, even if smaller, might be permanent, with industries to provide steady employment, income, and sustenance for the people.

Carrying out the sustained-yield principle is intelligent forestry and requires trained foresters. To prevent the continued loss of thousands of acres of valuable timber annually calls for fire prevention and for protection against forest insects and diseases; it depends for success upon carefully regulated cutting; and it may also require artificial reforestation of areas that have been too severely burned to reseed naturally.

Sustained-yield forestry often involves timber-stand improvement; that is, removal of some trees from the stand so as to favor the growth of those that are more valuable. Timber-stand improvement, to be of significance and to avoid destroying other possible values of forest lands, must be undertaken intelligently and carefully.

A suggestion has been made in a volume of Parkins and Whitaker, *Our Natural Resources and Their Conservation* (pages 104-114),* that may be worthy of consideration in reclaiming and restoring to use some of the hilly deforested lands in the eastern United States. This suggestion, based on the experience of Europe and northern Africa, is to grow without tillage trees bearing valuable nuts and barks used in industry. After the trees are established, the crops can be made to yield the small landowner a satisfactory return. Carob trees growing on rocky hillsides in Spain, Portugal, Algeria, Tunis, and other Mediterranean countries are cited as an example. These produce the carob beans, which are known as locust, and for at least 2,000 years have been a standard article of food in those countries. The chestnut groves of Corsica and the cork forests of Spain and Portugal also exemplify tree industries of the type that might be developed in this country.

It would require departure from traditional American methods to develop such industries, but the fact that thousands of people in Europe and Africa are living on forest products from trees growing on uncultivated hillsides, is worthy of consideration in our study of the best disposition that can be made of some of the lands that are now producing little or nothing of economic value. Chapter 5 of the volume just mentioned is on "Tree Crops," by Russell Smith, and, to say the least, is thought provoking and deserves careful reading.

* Parkins, A. E., and Whitaker, J. R. (editors). *Our Natural Resources and Their Conservation.* 650 pp., illus. New York, London, 1936. [Ed. 2, 1939.]

One conclusion reached by those who have studied the problem of forest conservation is that eventually a larger proportion of the wooded lands in America should be managed by public agencies, Federal, state, and local, but that many of the most productive of these lands should remain in private ownership, provided they are managed intelligently. Surveys indicate that exclusive of farm woodlots, small individual holdings scattered throughout the Mississippi Valley, and shelter-belt plantings in the Great Plains, about 100,000,000 acres should be added to the national forest and 50,000,000 acres to state and community forests. This would still leave between 200,000,000 and 300,000,000 acres of the best forest lands in private ownership.

6 / Relationship Between Forestry and Wildlife

The forest lands of this country now contain the largest of our remaining herds of elk, deer, moose, and other big-game animals. Other essentially forest mammals are the grizzly bear, black bear, mountain lion, and bobcat, and among fur bearers the fisher, marten, wolverine, and beaver. Forest-loving species among the larger birds commonly considered game are the wild turkey, blue grouse, and ruffed grouse. Numerous smaller mammals and birds, of course, are forest denizens.

With the exception of the deer, most of the remaining big-game animals are in the West, the only notable exception being the moose of Maine and northern Minnesota. The elk and moose long ago were shot out of the more accessible parts of their range, but they could not have continued there in any event, because forest lands large enough to harbor such wide-ranging species have been broken up and destroyed.

Value of Forest Openings

There are vast differences in the values of forests for game ranges. Dense virgin forest is of little use for game except as a shelter and retreat between periods of feeding. This statement can be amply verified by an inspection of the remaining virgin stands of spruce, fir, and redwood in the Pacific Northwest. Through these gloomy, mature forests of giant trees one may travel for miles without seeing any wildlife except a few specialized birds and small mammals.

Lack of animal life also characterizes some of the older hardwood forests in the eastern states. In one of those, I was once on a game preserve where snow had been on the ground for a week, and in half a day's tramp did not detect the track of a single big game animal. When one stops to analyze the situation, the reasons for the dearth of wildlife become clear. In crowded stands of timber the crowns of the trees are too high to be browsed. Moreover, the dense shade created by these chiefly contiguous crowns smothers out most of the shrubbery and herbage that might provide food for browsing animals or seeds or fruit for other wildlife. Biologists have long recognized that an unbroken stand of mature forest is much nearer a biological desert than are the sandy wastes of popular imagination. In deserts such as those of the southwestern states, the variety and number of birds and mammals to the acre are far greater than in dense mature forests.

Forest animals are generally those described as edge-inhabiting species. They congregate about the borders of forests and in woodland openings, for there they find a greater variety and abundance of the plants that furnish both shelter and sustenance. Anyone who has hunted animals for sport or who has tried to observe them for pleasure knows that he can find more kinds where there is plenty of ground vegetation. This is true of birds as well as of mammals. A recent "burn" grown up to brush and perennial vegetation often has a far greater population of mammals than has an equal area of virgin forest. Cut-over lands also are favorable up to the time the canopy begins to close. By contrast, the closely grown-up forest is of much less value for wildlife.

Effect of Forest Management on Wildlife

In recent years changes in forestry practices have been emphatically to the advantage of wildlife. The multiple-use concept, according to which all possible uses of the forest are considered in its administration, takes definite cognizance of the value of wildlife. This policy has been adopted in recent years by the United States Forest Service, by some of the state foresters and on some of the private forest lands owned by some of the more progressive forest industrial firms.

An order issued by a forester in charge of national forests in the Mississippi Valley illustrates this viewpoint. It directed that no glade or natural opening in a forest of less than ten acres should be planted to trees, and that on large cut-over or burned-over areas suitable plots should be left unplanted, so that as the trees developed they might be interspersed with openings having a variety of vegetation available to wildlife. This definite planning for the future needs indicates concretely the value to wildlife of the multiple-use concept.

The sustained-yield policy also fits admirably into a program of wildlife conservation. Having outlined this principle in the last chapter, it is sufficient here to say that it involves the employment of such cutting methods as always to leave enough usable and harvestable timber available to support dependent industries and communities permanently. The purpose, of course, is to provide community and individual security to the people who are dependent on forest products for their livelihood. Intentionally or otherwise, the man or men who worked out this principle have at the same time contributed toward security for wildlife. In fact, had they been considering wildlife needs alone, they could not have worked out a better basic principle for the cutting of timber.

This principle has been applied to advantage by the Virginia Commission of Game and Inland Fisheries, under its cooperative agreement with the U. S. Forest Service. Each sportsman hunting or fishing in the national forests in Virginia is required to purchase a special use stamp, receipts from the sales of which are applied toward fish and game management on the national forests. Cutting operations are planned in consultation with state biologists for maximum benefits to wildlife. The plan has been successful in increasing the number of deer, wild turkeys, and grouse in the forests without interfering with timber production.

In developing the relationship between wildlife and sustained-yield forestry, it is necessary to use certain generalizations. Let us consider a broad expanse of forest land from which all the merchantable timber has been harvested, on which the remainder has been knocked down by logging (and perhaps burning), and where reproduction is starting again from the beginning. The bare tract will at first produce annual weeds and perennials. In a few seasons bushes of various kinds and certain types of trees will commence to appear. Gradually, unless frequent burning takes place, the forest is reëstablished. The stand of trees will thicken, slowly close the canopy, and tend to choke out much of the underbrush and herbaceous vegetation. This is particularly true in the heavy softwood forests of the Pacific coast, although in the longleaf pine forests of the South and the ponderosa pine forests of the Intermountain States the trees do not grow closely enough to shade the ground completely. Competition of the trees with the smaller and shallow-rooted plants for soil moisture and fertility, however, has somewhat the same effect as overshading in the more closely growing types of forests.

After the canopy closes, the forest becomes progressively less valuable for wildlife and will so continue during the actively growing period of the trees, which under the sustained-yield principle may be as much as a hundred years. At any time when the forest is mature enough to produce first-class merchantable timber it may be cut again. After cutting, with the growth of a much greater quantity of ground vegetation, food and cover for wildlife will be increased manyfold. If there is a nucleus of wildlife under the again favorable conditions, deer, grouse, turkeys, and other woodland dwellers will multiply quickly, and during the period of brush and sapling growth the population thus built up will approach the carrying capacity of the land.

As the canopy again closes and food supplies diminish, the deer and other terrestrial creatures face a crisis: they must either move out or starve. Very often there is no place for them to go, and then many thousands die. As the climax of the new forest growth approaches, wildlife will decline and remain at a minimum until the forest is again cut over.

Selective and Clear Cutting

On the sustained-yield basis there are at least two methods of harvesting timber that will immediately benefit wildlife. One will increase the total production of food on a given area, and the other will result in better distribution of this food in the forest.

The first is called selective cutting. It involves a continuous selection throughout forests of trees that have reached merchantable age. The openings thus created in the canopy encourage a growth of new ground vegetation and of shrubs or small trees. Where the timber on large tracts can be profitably cut by this method, food conditions should be better for many species of forest wildlife. Such cutting tends to scatter populations throughout the forest rather than concentrate them in the areas of best food.

The second type of harvesting involves the clear cutting of tracts scattered throughout the forested area. From the wildlife standpoint, once a full management plan is in operation, the smaller and the more widely scattered the tracts, the nearer they are to an idealized food and cover condition. It is known that this breaking up of forests into blocks of trees of different ages or age classes is often good forestry. The limiting factor on the size and distribution of the clear-cut areas is economic. The topography of the land, means of transportation, type of logging, cost of operations, and prices obtainable are some of the obvious factors that make it impossible to conform to any one definite practice in all forests.

These clear-cut areas, of course, immediately resume the cycle of annuals and perennials, shrubs, and trees and add to the quantity and variety of food available for wildlife in the entire forest. When widely scattered, such clear-cut areas have the same effect, in bringing about a more equal dispersion of individual animals throughout the area. Once a complete cutting cycle has passed over such a unit, its annual production of food will tend to become closer to the average production and will also tend strongly to avoid the abrupt changes in animal populations that are caused by varying food supplies.

Distribution of cuttings is of considerable significance in wildlife management. If the area cut each year were contiguous to that cut the year before, the tendency would be to concentrate the animals exactly as in the case of the previous illustration of one huge cut-over or burned-over area. Such a condition would probably result in a big building up of various species and their consequent abrupt decline as the area grew back into forest and became less productive of wildlife.

The revegetation of the first 20 to 30 years on many types of forest land produces the best food and cover conditions for deer. Therefore, the percentage of the total area available for maximum use by these animals (used only as an illustration) depends on the length of the cutting cycle established under the sustained-yield plan. In 40- to 60-year cycles, one-third to one-half of the area would always be in good condition for producing deer food. In longer cycles the production of this food would be proportionately less.

Wildlife enthusiasts and forest and wildlife managers must realize that the type of logging, length of cycle, and size of the areas that are clear-cut, if that is the method used, will of necessity depend primarily on economic or forestry factors rather than on wildlife needs. The encouraging thing is that whichever method is used, the result will be an improvement for wildlife, compared with conditions that would exist if a uniform forest of even age were allowed to occupy the land indefinitely. Moreover, foresters will probably practice these types of cutting on an increasing scale, as it is known that to scatter age classes as widely as possible is not only good forestry but benefits wildlife as well.

Natural Clearings

Fortunately, relatively few present-day forests have stands of timber so dense as to exclude wildlife from great areas, although great coniferous plantings in some states may ultimately reach that condition. Openings here and there in normal stands of timber are made by any of a number of causes. There are rocky ridges and cliffs in most mountain forests that do not grow trees but do produce shrubs and other vegetation of cover and food value for wildlife. There are gravelly or infertile areas that will not support tree growth, and spots where the soil moisture is insufficient for trees. Death of individual trees due to insects and diseases opens the forest canopy, and whenever a tree falls a little spot of ground vegetation appears. In actuality, few forests present solid canopies extending for miles, and the conditions accompanying extreme forest density are rarely found.

The existence of these natural openings simplifies the problem of the forester who attempts so to manage an area as to produce both timber and wildlife. The application of either method of sustained-yield harvesting makes for sound economic conditions and is almost certain to provide a fairly adequate distribution of wildlife throughout the forest.

Deer Management in Forests

A relationship between browsing animals and forestry that must not be overlooked is that excess populations of deer, elk, or other game may seriously damage the forest and prevent its reproduction. The history of the Kaibab deer herd in Arizona is an outstanding illustration of the fact that the building up of a herd beyond the carrying capacity of the land exhausts the food supply and results in the elimination to a serious extent of many of the more valuable browse plants and in very greatly reducing or even annihilating forest reproduction. The overpopulation of the Kaibab not only seriously interfered with the forest but eventually brought disaster to the deer herd itself. There have been many similar situations in recent years scattered throughout the deer range and the public is slowly learning that it is possible to have too many deer in a given area. The wide distribution of food supplies and consequently of wildlife over a forest has the tendency to prevent such abnormal increases in numbers as occurred on the Kaibab.

A classic example of the successful utilization of cut-over lands and young forests in developing herds of deer is found in Pennsylvania. From a nucleus of 50 animals in 1906, that state, in the next 19 years, imported and released 1,192 white-tailed deer. The state conservation officials established a rigid protective system, and with the aid of an adequate police force, supported by public sentiment, built up in a few years a tremendous deer herd on its cut-over lands.

The condition above all others, however, that made this increase possible was that Pennsylvania, at the time this work was undertaken, had great areas of cut-over lands that were in almost ideal condition for deer producion. Today, however, we observe the unfavorable results of cut-over lands growing up to mature trees, with the consequent decrease in available food—the very condition that scattered cutting or selective cutting for such uses as were possible for such young trees, together with more adequate harvests of the deer crop, would have at least greatly reduced.

It is obvious from this discussion that certain types of wildlife, mainly the browsing species of big game, can have a very deleterious effect on the forest, just as certain forestry practices can have a detrimental effect on the abundance of the animals.

Effect of Rodents on the Forest

There are other relationships between forests and wildlife that should be emphasized in this chapter. Rodents play a definite part in forest economy. Their influence may be either good or bad. Depending on locality and forest conditions, they may be either forest planters or preventers of reforestation. On some western areas studied by the U. S. Fish and Wildlife Service, the population of seed-eating rodents has been so high as practically to preclude reforestation. This is particularly noticeable in such forests as those of ponderosa pine and of related trees that produce comparatively large seeds. Among the ponderosa pines the abundance of mice and chipmunks may be so great as to take the bulk of the seed crop produced even in good years. In seasons of poor seed production, the rodents resort more to seeds of weeds and shrubs, but as they prefer those of the yellow pine they find and devour almost all of them.

On the other hand, the activities of chipmunks, squirrels, and mice in burying seeds often result in plantings in favorable spots. When one of these small hoarders is taken by a predator, or killed in any of the innumerable accidents that beset them, the seeds it has hidden securely in the ground may sprout and develop into trees. Local conditions will determine whether the net effect of the rodent population on forest reproduction is good or bad.

A concrete example of the rodent-forest relationship may be cited. In cut-over lands that had grown up for years to chaparral and brush, it was found that all the pine seed that naturally reached the areas was taken by an overpopulation of white-footed mice. Even artificial plantings of seedlings were promptly taken. Reduction of these rodents, however, was quickly followed by a reëstablishment of trees, either from artificial planting of seed or seedlings or by natural reproduction in areas that were not too distant from trees sufficiently mature to bear seed.

Forests and Birds

Blackbirds and meadowlarks, which migrate in swarms through the longleaf pine regions, sometimes have a detrimental effect on the forest, in some years taking altogether too large a percentage of the seed to permit good reproduction. Seed crops are not consumed every year, however, and an annual growth of young pines is not necessary. The problem as to how much permanent damage rodents and birds cause by seed destruction is certainly not one to be solved by superficial observations.

Certain birds have a definite relationship to forests. Woodpeckers frequent trees that have died or are dying from disease or insect attacks and feed extensively on the insects present there. These birds undoubtedly have a suppressive influence on forest-insect pests, but when an outbreak has reached the epidemic stage they cannot cope with it to the extent of preventing serious losses. Their influence is much greater when the insect population is normal than when, by some combination of circumstances, it has grown up rapidly to the epidemic stage. This is true of many other species of birds that feed on the kinds of insects that affect the foliage or bark of trees. These include vireos, warblers, chickadees, nuthatches, and titmice—a variety of small forest-inhabiting birds. The rôle of insect-eating birds in protecting forests undoubtedly has sometimes been over-emphasized, but certainly we can say that the tendency of their feeding habits is good and is in the right direction.

Forest Game-Bird Management

Game birds, including grouse and wild turkeys, eat fewer insects, as they greatly relish buds, leaves and wild fruits, but they rarely, if ever, have been noted to have any detrimental effect on forests. Forests are vital to their livelihood, but they must be of an open type. The birds mostly frequent edges and openings, but in emergencies they may seek shelter in the denser parts. The reason is not far to seek, for it is the more open parts of the forest that produce in greatest variety the trees and shrubs that furnish the fruits, seeds, buds, and green vegetation so important to the birds. During the summer months game birds are heavy consumers of fruits and succulent vegetation, mixed, when occasion offers, with insects; and during the winter months, they resort to buds, twigs, dried fruits, seeds, acorns, and nuts.

Obviously the wider the variety of trees and shrubs in an area the greater are the possible sources of food supply for grouse, turkeys, and other birds of similar requirements. Variety rather than uniformity in vegetation is best for their welfare. Planting large areas to a single species of tree is therefore detrimental to such birds. Mixed plantings, in imitation of natural growths, are much more valuable. Plantings restricted to a few selected timber trees will not yield crops as satisfactory for wildlife as will a greater variety of species. Trees producing fruits that are either eagerly eaten by the birds in their season or that hang on the trees and furnish a reserve food supply for the winter months include dogwood, black gum, wild cherries of various kinds, oaks, particularly those that produce small acorns, beech, viburnum, hawthorn, and wild plums. Many of the shrubs and vines that grow in the forests throughout the country also are of value to wildlife in many ways.

Too intensive forestry, by suppressing trees and shrubs regarded as of inferior commercial value, tends to reduce the variety of species that support wildlife. Any timber-stand improvement that also favors the commercially valuable trees by cutting out species less valuable may affect the future abundance of wildlife in a forest so treated. If drastic, it may greatly reduce or alter the populations. The work needs to be planned with much care it it is not to do a great deal of harm to game and other species. Areas have been observed where timber-stand improvement has been carried to such a length that the forest is made much less usable by wildlife.

Forest Fur Animals

The management of the fur-bearing animals of the forest is probably the most neglected phase of American conservation. Forest land is a fertile field for such management, as the conditions there are generally favorable for the production of a fur crop. If a supply of the more valuable species, including the beaver, marten, wolverine, and fisher, the furs of which are always high priced, is to be continued, forest lands must produce them. So far as the beaver, one of the most valuable and the most easily handled of all of these fur animals, is concerned, many of the details of management have been worked out. Beavers have been successfully reintroduced throughout much of their former range in the forested regions of the United States, largely within the past twenty-five years. Thriving colonies can be found throughout New England, along the Appalachian Mountains as well as throughout most of the western forests and in many states of the Mississippi Valley. They have been successfully transplanted from lowlands into mountain areas. Transplanting operations have a twofold purpose: One, that of removing the animals from areas where they were doing damage to agricultural interests; the other, placing them in forested stream basins where their dams serve to conserve water. These practices, plus good protection, have built up beaver populations almost to pest status in some states. In such cases a more adequate harvest of these animals has become good management.

The difficulties in the way of increasing the supply of other species of fur bearers in the national forests do not result so much from biological problems as from conflicting jurisdiction as to protection and lack of interest on the part of state administrators of wildlife; however, in various cases, there may be many biological problems to be solved. The field is neglected and is one that could be cultivated to the great profit of the American people.

Forestry and Fish Life

Forested lands contain most of the trout streams and many of the finest fishing lakes in America. In general they shelter the waters that, being the least polluted, still present the nearest approach to natural conditions for the propagation and perpetuation of fish life. Fish conservation does not involve such serious problems in relation to forestry as does the handling of big game, fur, and other wildlife, and therefore it has already developed in the forests further and faster than has the management of other forms of wildlife. In the western mountains large numbers of lakes that formerly were devoid of fishes, because they were above the high waterfalls in the mountain streams that no fish could pass, have now been stocked with various types of trouts, or even with other fishes, and so provide food and recreation not only to the people of nearby districts but also to many who come from long distances.

If sport fishing is to be perpetuated in many districts, it must be provided to a large extent by the streams and lakes of forested lands. Forestry practices may help or hinder angling in any particular stream. Road builders often have a tendency to follow stream valleys, where less difficulty is encountered in finding suitable grades. Cutting a road along a trout stream, however, may ruin it entirely by destroying the vegetative cover, dumping construction débris into the stream, and causing erosion from cut banks. Removal of the cover may raise the temperature of the water to a point destructive to trout. All roadways along such streams have the disadvantage also of facilitating access to practically every foot of the stream, thus encouraging overfishing and rendering it almost impossible to maintain a supply of fish in the adjacent waters.

On the other hand, reforesting many thousands of acres of cut-over and denuded lands and protecting them from fire are great assets to fishing. The forests grow up and again regulate the run-off, thus allowing the streams to maintain more constant levels and more even temperatures, keeping silt out of them, and making all conditions better for fish life. The reforestation movement has been of great advantage to fishing, and forest managers generally have taken an interest in the improvement of streams.

Fire Protection

Fire is potentially a deadly enemy of both the forest and wildlife. In a few hours it may destroy forest growth that has taken many years to develop. Where the land is intensely burned over, the vegetable content of the soil and the seeds of trees are frequently so thoroughly destroyed as to make reforestation a slow, even imperceptible, process. Over a hundred years ago a great fire in Oregon that swept from the Williamette Valley through the Coast Ranges to the Pacific burned so fiercely and so long that it destroyed most of the humus and seeds and left scars that are plainly visible today. Only in spots where it jumped over little patches of timber or in sheltered canyons that preserved a few trees is there any noticeable natural reforestation. Great areas of this burn are still occupied by tangled masses of ferns, blackberries, and other low vegetation, and normal reforestation will be a slow process.

Rapid running forest fires, particularly crown fires, may be very destructive to wildlife. If they occur in the nesting season of birds, the broods of the year and often even the breeding stock are destroyed. Many parent birds, particularly those setting on eggs that are nearly ready to hatch, will stay on the nests until suffocated or burned. Even the fishes do not escape forest fires. Ashes falling into the water or carried into the streams with the run-off produce strong chemical solutions that destroy not only fish food but also often the fishes themselves.

Upland wildlife recovers from a burn long before the forest does, for the new growth of temporary vegetation furnishes feeding grounds for many species of wild birds and mammals that in heavy forest cover could not exist in abundance.

These conditions apply particularly to wild, or uncontrolled, fires. Another class, which may be used as a management tool, has certain beneficial effects. In recent years in the southern longleaf pine areas, it has been found that controlled fire is beneficial both to wildlife and to forest reproduction. Such fire, by removing the heavy mantle of dead grass before longleaf pine seeds fall, promotes the establishment of seedlings. Moreover, light burning every two or three years has been found beneficial in stands of young longleaf pines heavily infested with the brown-spot needle disease.

The work of Stoddard* during the Coöperative Quail Investigation and studies carried on since have demonstrated conclusively that the major limiting factors on the abundance of quails, turkeys, and other southern upland game birds are lack of winter food and a superabundance of cover, particularly of broomsedge, which crowds

* Stoddard, Herbert L. *The Bobwhite Quail: Its Habits, Preservation, and Increase.* 559 pp., illus. New York, 1931.

out valuable food plants and also affords shelter to the cotton rat, one of the most prolific enemies of small ground-nesting birds. From experience in managing a large area of plantation land for wildlife, Stoddard recommends burning lightly and in such manner that the entire tract is spotburned every three or four years. By destroying the matted broomsedge, a much more valuable stand of plants, including a number of legumes, that furnish food and cover to the game birds is secured. It has become apparent also that burning at frequent intervals lessens the abundance of ticks and chiggers, which also have a detrimental effect on wildlife.

Generally speaking, however, on the basis of present knowledge, fire is so great an enemy of both wildlife and forests that there is an increasing amount of fire control, both on public and on private forest lands. This should in the long run be exceedingly beneficial to wildlife.

From the foregoing discussion it should be evident that forest conservation and wildlife conservation are closely interwoven. A forest is a biotic community made up of the total population of its living things, both plant and animal. Any management practice affecting any part of such a community may well affect other elements either for good or for evil. Many of these interrelationships are still not clearly understood, but enough is known to indicate the close tie-up between forestry and the preservation and management of forest wildlife. Management plans must take cognizance of both. The two cannot be separated.

7 / Wildlife on Agricultural Lands

In the early part of the twentieth century those interested in wildlife were greatly concerned about the future of big game in the United States but worried little about the wildlife that was found about human habitation and on agricultural lands. There was good reason for this. A combination of factors, including over-exploitive forestry, over-grazing and over-killing of big game by market hunters, had all but wiped out the herds in many sections. Since that time, as outlined in other chapters of this book, many big game species have made a dramatic comeback. Better forestry, particularly better fire control, better law enforcement which greatly reduced market hunting, long closed seasons, restocking, and a buck law, have restored many big game herds. The return of these animals has brought new problems, but they are often problems of abundance rather than problems of scarcity. Few wildlife managers even with their present-day headaches would go back to the scarcity days if they had any choice.

A directly opposite condition prevailed in wildlife on agricultural lands. Except for a relatively few areas in one-crop cash farming districts, the agricultural lands were operated as family-sized farms. Many of them had hedgerows or fences grown up to weeds or shrubs that furnished winter cover and some food for the wildlife; methods of harvest, tillage, and land use were such that they left an abundance of waste grain and weed seeds on the ground or in the fencerows as wildlife food through the critical winter months. For these reasons and many others, farm wildlife was relatively abundant and occasioned little concern except in the minds of a few extreme "alarmists" who could foresee the decline of these species.

There have been numerous estimates as to the proportion of hunting furnished by farm game, and these estimates vary from state to state. In the states having large areas of agricultural land, there is no question but that farm game furnishes much of the potential if not the actual hunting opportunity. Species that are widely distributed and generally considered farm game are squirrels and rabbits among the mammals and, to a lesser degree, others such as raccoons and opossums, which are hunted by a relatively limited number of people. Among the birds, the mourning dove, bobwhite, and pheasant are pre-eminently the farm game birds with others relatively of little hunting importance. Other farm wildlife as a whole was abundant. The hedgerows and woodlots were filled with small birds and mammals. The open fields were occupied by other species of birds and mammals that favored this type of habitat.

Changed farming practices often have greatly affected the relative abundance of these farmland species of wildlife, and this has been due to many causes. The major ones perhaps are the development of the soil conservation program by the U. S. Soil Conservation Service, the Agricultural Conservation Payments program which under various names has been in existence for a long period and which seems to be destined to go on indefinitely, the development of potent and stable agricultural chemicals for control of insects, rodents, and weeds, and the development of industrial farming in many sections of the country.

Soil Conservation

The soil conservation program working through local soil conservation districts, which include most of the agricultural land in the nation, can be expected to have a far-reaching effect on farm wildlife. As this program is now operated, the Soil Conservation Service furnishes technical assistance to landowners within these districts. Among other activities the single one that seems to have the greatest potential wildlife effect is the farm plan that will be prepared for each farm unit. The present basis of these plans is a land capability classification in which the land is separated into eight categories, according to its use capabilities. The first four classifications are those suitable for cultivation, while the final four are suitable for permanent pasture, woodland, or other vegetation. Since they are the basic philosophy on which most of the soil conservation work is planned, they should be listed here.

A. Suitable for cultivation
   - I. Without special practices.
   - II. With simple practices such as contour cultivation, strip cropping.
   - III. With complex or intensive practices such as terraces and usually a combination of other practices.
   - IV. With intensive practices and limited use, usually long rotations with no intertilled crops.

B. Not suitable for cultivation
   - V. Without special practices. This land is suitable for grazing or cutting of forest without special practices to protect the lands.
   - VI. With moderate restrictions of use. Land that is moderately susceptible to deterioration. Rotation grazing, logging with careful location of trails and other practices are necessary to protect the soils.
   - VII. With severe restriction on use. Land highly susceptible to deterioration. On range only occasional grazing; in forests, only highly selective logging.

C. Not suitable for cultivation, pasture, or woodland. Suitable for wildlife.
   - VIII. With or without special practices, suitable for the production of various types of wildlife.

While the theory of using land according to its capabilities is logical from an agricultural standpoint, this classification if carried out literally and completely would relegate wildlife largely to the land that is not fit for anything else. However, there is little likelihood that this classification will ever be applied in its entirety to all farm lands.

Wildlife values on the first four classes will be limited to the kind of wildlife that can live and prosper in heavily used agricultural land. Hedgerows, odd corners, permanent vegetation where strip cropping is practiced, or permanent vegetation on terraces will provide some cover and food for wildlife. In many of the more intensively farmed areas, cover will be the limiting factor in the northern states, since agricultural crops of many kinds usually leave enough waste grain and other seed on the ground to provide for many species of wildlife.

Where this intensively utilized land is devoted to grass farming, all seed-eaters can be expected to decrease in most areas, while more omnivorous species of wildlife may continue to thrive. Small nocturnal mammals will be less directly affected, except as their food supply is changed by some of the agricultural practices.

The most frequent criticisms from a wildlife standpoint of soil conservation practices on land suitable for cultivation fall into three categories, depending upon the section of the country in which the practices are applied.

In the northern Great Plains there has been widespread criticism of the drainage of potholes and other wetlands under the Soil Conservation Service program.

In other sections there has been considerable criticism of the tearing out of hedges, usually on fence lines bordering rectangular fields. Wherever these fields are to be put in contour cultivation, particularly when fields are to be enlarged, much suitable wildlife habitat including winter cover, travel lanes, and nesting habitat have been destroyed. Sometimes these are replaced by new plantings; other times not.

In other sections there has been local criticism of the drainage of bottomlands and of the attempt to move the wildlife habitat to the poorer, rough slopes and hill lands along the streams. Needless to say, such a program makes drastic changes in the wildlife populations, both as to kinds and numbers.

The lands classified as suitable for permanent pasture, range, or woodland offer more possiblities for certain types of wildlife, particularly the areas classed as most valuable for woodland purposes. Certain species of wildlife will be favored by devoting land to permanent pasture or range and woodlands, whether as windbreaks, shelterbelts, farm woodlots, or cover for steep slopes.

The control of run-off sometimes requires the impoundment of small ponds in areas where water would naturally collect to form rills. These ponds often offer very favorable possibilities for wildlife habitat. The extent to which these various possibilities are developed depends upon the interest the landowner may have in wildlife.

It is not the purpose of this chapter to outline the techniques needed for wildlife developments to offset changing agricultural practices but rather to present the problems and possibilities that exist. In many states a close working relationship between the state wildlife agency and the soil conservation districts has been developed. It is almost a truism to say that in those states where competent men have been assigned to work closely with these districts, wildlife is getting a much better break than in the states in which such a cooperative arrangement is not present. Many states are providing suitable wildlife cover plants for use on the areas which are to be taken out of row crops and furnishing seeds or plants for use around ponds, odd corners, and other places which will not be farmed.

The addition of the small watersheds program to the responsibilities of the Soil Conservation Service has provided another opportunity for wildlife agencies to be in on the planning of land and water management programs that affect areas that usually cover several farms. Many alert wildlife agencies have entered into this program, and all others need to do so if these activities are to have a beneficial rather than an adverse effect upon wildlife.

Before this legislation was enacted, there was a growing appreciation of the fact that many land and water management problems could not be handled by an individual landowner, and such legislation was inevitable. Under the present law there is recognition of wildlife values, but it is necessary for wildlife agencies to take an active part in planning and executing the small watersheds programs if the possibilities that exist are to become realities.

While in general it is apparent that over the nation as a whole, soil conservation planning has far exceeded the actual application of the plans to the soil, the plans are being increasingly applied in whole or in part. It can be expected that eventually nearly all agricultural land will be operating under a soil conservation program. So far as farm game is concerned, the most obvious beneficial results come from terracing, contour plowing, and strip cropping on the rougher lands. Terraces and strip cropping with their permanent vegetation on some areas can furnish some of the cover that has disappeared from much of the land with changed agricultural and harvesting practices. The extent to which this has been applied varies greatly, but to one traveling by air, it is obvious that only a small part of the area needing some conservation practices has as yet been treated.

Most agricultural land is now in soil conservation districts, and most states have laws authorizing the organization of these self-governing local soil groups. They contain much potential good for wildlife, but this potential needs to be translated into action before it becomes of any actual value to wildlife. The exact approach to be taken depends upon the type of agriculture and the type of land, but in general the best approach has been to fit necessary wildlife practices into individual farm plans.

There is one obvious conclusion already resulting from this work; practices that are useful and acceptable in one part of the country may have little value elsewhere. Therefore, technicians working with people on the land must be alert to develop practices that will apply to the particular community in which they are working.

Wildlife conservationists have much to gain from the over-all soil conservation program because it provides the best logical program that has been developed to date for the use of our land and water resources. While the application of soil conservation practices may shift the wildlife populations around and sometimes destroy specialized habitat, it has some compensating factors that make it possible to have some wildlife value on many farm areas.

One other factor should be mentioned, however, and that is that the technicians who make farm plans are persons primarily interested in agriculture, and the type of plan they develop often depends upon their personal background and experience. There are few farm planners with the broad ecological backgrounds that are necessary if such plans are to be truly comprehensive. Many of the present farm planners are by training agronomists or livestock men or engineers, and their plans often reflect that training, sometimes to the detriment of other values. In such cases, it is up to the wildlife agencies to sell the farmer on modifications of the plan to provide the things that will benefit wildlife whenever it can be done without materially increasing the expense to the landowner or materially decreasing the income that he may receive.

Agricultural Conservation Payments

Agricultural conservation payments have complicated the wildlife problems on agricultural land, particularly the payments for draining marshes or for clearing brushland that is of value to wildlife. Such activities on a broad scale have been most in evidence in the Great Plains area, but they also occur elsewhere. Whether or not payment for this kind of work is justified in the national interest is a controversial subject that occupies much time and attention of wildlife technicians, landowners, and newspapers in the sections involved. From a wildlife standpoint, however, there is no doubt of the result.

Drainage of potholes in the northern plains which are breeding marshes for waterfowl represents a net loss to the continental waterfowl population. It is known that these potholes, acre for acre, produce more birds than the larger marshes which have been restored or preserved, and there is a strong movement to include these smaller marshes in a management and preservation program.

Likewise in many areas the destruction of brush and other suitable

THERE ARE FORESTS AND FORESTS

Plate 9 / The Joshua trees on the Mohave Desert in California (above) and the hardwoods in the East (below) illustrate the great variety of forest areas in the United States

(Forest Service photos: 363695 by A. E. Wieslander; 227104 by Bernard S. Meyer.)

EACH FOREST HAS ITS WILDLIFE

Plate 10 / The remarkable virgin stand of longleaf pine in Mississippi (above) could not support the marsh-loving moose (below), which is dependent on a different type of forest.

(Forest Service photo 310743 by Paul S. Carter; Fish and Wildlife Service photo B38397 by Olaus J. Murie.)

BEARS AND DEER ARE FOREST GAME

Plate 11 / The black bear in Yellowstone National Park, Wyoming, and the white-tailed deer in Michigan, photographed at night, represent two outstanding wildlife resources of the forests.

(Fish and Wildlife Service photos: B881M by M. P. Skinner: B1042M by George Shiras III.)

THEY LIVE IN THE FORESTS

Plate 12 / Game birds and fur animals of the forests include the wild turkey and Richardson's grouse (above) and the fisher and marten (below).

(Fish and Wildlife Service photos: B54695 by Leo K. Couch; B35880 by Olaus J. Murie; B285M by Nelson H. Kent; B2721M, photographer unknown.)

TOO MANY DEER SPOIL THE FOREST

Plate 13 / Plentiful undergrowth in a forest with openings provides ideal deer range (below), but if deer become too abundant they over-browse the forest, leaving no food below a so-called "deer line" (above).

(Fish and Wildlife Service photos: B57197 by Leo K. Couch: B99M by Thomas Blagden.)

DUST STORMS MAKE WILDLIFE DESERTS

Plate 14 / A dust bowl (above), left by dust storms (below) after grasslands have been unwisely exploited, is as unattractive to wildlife as it is to man.

(Soil Conservation Service photos: Okla350A by Eddie L. Moore; Colo3605 by Thomas G. Meier.)

BISON AND PRONGHORN ROAMED THE GRASSLANDS

Plate 15 / The buffalo and prong-horned antelope, once plentiful, dwindled with man's occupation of the grasslands but are now increasing on such areas as the National Bison Range in Montana (above) and the Charles Sheldon Antelope Refuge in Nevada (below).

(Fish and Wildlife Service photos: B21741 by G. W. Field; B44889 by Ernest J. Greenwalt.)

CARIBOU AND WAPITI ARE BIG GAME

Plate 16 / Both big-game animals of the deer family, the wapiti, or elk (below), is a resident animal that shifts its feeding grounds locally with the season, whereas the caribou of Alaska (above) makes extended migrations in its seasonal rounds of feeding grounds.

(Fish and Wildlife Service photos B24140 and B36952 by Olaus J. Murie.)

wildlife cover and food plants to create additional and sometimes poor grade farmland has a direct and devastating effect upon local wildlife populations. The lower Rio Grande and the semi-arid lands adjoining it to the north are an area in which much of the habitat for the indigenous species of wildlife, such as the chachalaca, the white-winged dove, and many interesting non-game birds, have been greatly reduced over large areas as a result of brush clearing.

Where these agricultural conservation payments are superimposed upon the soil conservation program, it sometimes happens that disastrous wildlife effects are produced. Wildlife managers have not yet found a way to counteract this in any great degree, although a number of different approaches are now being tried.

The most recent effort has been the creation of the soil conservation reserve, known as the Soil Bank. Under this legislation either a part or all of a farm may be retired from the production of surplus crops. This land can be utilized for several purposes, among them the planting of forest trees or the provision of wildlife habitat. The payments offered as inducement vary from place to place, but it is possible to enter into contracts running for ten years or more if the conservation practices are maintained.

Many state wildlife agencies are participating in this program in the hope that it will help offset some of the adverse effects on wildlife that have accompanied other agricultural changes. It is not possible to evaluate the results of this program as this is written, but it seems obvious that placing these islands of food or cover in intensively farmed areas will have a beneficial effect upon some local wildlife populations.

Industrial Farming

Industrial farming is likewise a phenomenon which has mushroomed in recent years. With the development of bigger and more efficient machinery, larger acreages of land can now be farmed by one individual or by one set of equipment. In many areas this has meant tearing out of fences and hedgerows, in developing larger fields that can be handled economically and efficiently with these big machines. This has largely come about since the inception of the depression farm program of the early 1930's, the subsidies paid providing enough of a margin to make the gamble of planting huge acreages, particularly in the one-crop sections of the country, worth while. The effects upon wildlife can be startling and in some areas wildlife is largely eliminated. This includes not only game birds but songbirds of many varieties and small mammals as well. While there may be plenty of waste grain or other seeds for food, there is little cover remaining when the new cultural and harvesting machinery is utilized.

While the most spectacular development of industrial farming has occurred in the Great Plains and in some parts of the South and West, there is a general tendency to enlarge individual farms. The huge investment in modern machinery and the capability, once it is acquired, of handling more land has caused a general trend toward enlarging individual farms. This usually results in larger fields and a desire to take out of them, so far as possible, every wet place or tree that interferes with the maximum efficiency of these machines.

From a wildlife standpoint this means the decrease of many species that require special habitats or that habitually feed close to cover. The larger the fields the fewer acres will be suitable for such species. It may mean an increase in numbers for the relatively few species that prefer large open areas of habitat.

If wildlife agencies can successfully work with individual landowners or groups of them to provide practices to offset this trend, some wildlife populations may be maintained, but the prospects are not too bright in some areas.

Pesticides

The fourth major change that has caused the present concern for small farm wildlife is the enormous growth of the use of very potent new chemicals for the control of insects, rodents, plant diseases, and unwanted vegetation. While there is much public agitation over the use of pesticides, largely because in many instances they are applied by airplane and the results are more easily observed by the average citizen, there is growing concern among biologists as to the ultimate effect of such chemicals upon wildlife populations and upon the biological balance of the land itself.

Spectacular kills of wildlife, both with the use of rodenticides and insecticides are a matter of record. With the development of the exceedingly toxic stable chlorinated hydrocarbons which may retain their killing power for months or years, there is more and more concern as to the ultimate effects of even a limited use of these potent chemicals.

In a few cases there are formulae for the use of these chemicals that are based on careful tests. With DDT, for example, it is known that the use of less than one pound to an acre will not immediately affect bird or mammal life, although the same strength mixtures used in streams or ponds will cause partial or complete destruction of the fish and aquatic life in that water. Indeed, some of the most spectacular examples of kills have been those of fish in some of the better known fishing waters of Canada and the United States. There are, however, scores of insecticides many times as toxic as DDT on which there have been no careful tests of their effect on wildlife.

Often it is not only the wildlife itself but the food supply that is directly concerned. Studies have been published which show that not only have many fish been killed, but the aquatic insects and other small life upon which they depend were practically absent after the use of some of these pesticides.

This would be serious enough if the chemical were always applied at the rate specified. However, too many operators and landowners go on the theory that if one pound per acre is good, two or five pounds is that much better and govern themselves accordingly. Some of the most spectacular kills yet reported have been found to be based upon excessive use of chemicals, although some heavy kills have been reported when some of the more toxic chemicals are used by official agencies at supposedly safe rates.

Of growing concern, however, is the apparent residual effects which continue to kill long after the original treatment. No one knows as yet how long after treatment this lethal effect continues, although there is some evidence that some insecticides will kill birds at least a year after application. Also the question is being raised increasingly by biologists as to the effect of continual application to agricultural land of some of these chemicals even in sub-lethal dosages. There are some observations which show clearly that ingestion of small amounts of some of these potent chlorinated hydrocarbons may reduce reproductive capacity even if it does not harm the individual bird or small mammal that takes it.

Experimental feeding of test birds under carefully controlled conditions has demonstrated conclusively that even small amounts of some of the chlorinated hydrocarbons result in reduced fertility of eggs and poor survival of the chicks that are hatched. Several studies have shown that populations of robins and other ground-feeding birds have been eliminated by spraying for control of the elm bark beetle. These studies have shown that earthworms store enough of these toxic materials either to kill the birds that eat them or to destroy their reproductive capacity as much as a year after the spraying operation.

There is a growing belief that the drastic decline of the herons and other wading birds, and such species as the bald eagle, is a result of the widespread use of these chemicals in mosquito control. The decline may come from a direct kill of the birds or from the destruction over wide areas of the aquatic forms on which they feed. There is as yet no conclusive evidence published that this is true, but there is some field observation to substantiate it.

The organic phosphates, another new group of toxic compounds, are equally deadly to birds, mammals, and other forms when first applied, but they break down quickly and consequently do not cause the long-time hazard that comes from more stable compounds.

In addition to these two groups, there are other new and lethal compounds used to a much more limited extent that are hazardous to wildlife.

Many of these compounds, especially the chlorinated hydrocarbons, can be stored in the bodies of warm-blooded animals. The ultimate effect of this storage is as yet unknown except that there is definite evidence that in some species it impairs the reproductive functions.

A growing number of biologists and entomologists are concerned with the fact that these pesticides are nonselective; in other words, they not only kill the species against which they are directed, but their natural enemies as well. There is some evidence also that such sprays may help some of the more resistant pests by eliminating their more susceptible insect enemies. Many biologists also point to the fact that both mosquitoes and flies, two groups against which these substances have been widely used, have developed strains that are now immune. This would seem to indicate the futility of continued use of such substances, although the agencies responsible for the operations are often slow to recognize the facts.

While not of direct concern to wildlife managers, it is noteworthy that the Public Health Service and a growing number of physicians are recognizing both a direct and indirect hazard to man in the widespread use of such toxic materials. Some chemical companies also recognize the bad effects of the use of their products, at least to the extent of trying to develop materials that are more selective.

Of equal concern in some areas is the growing use of chemical herbicides to destroy unwanted vegetation. There have been some proposals to denude some of the mountainous areas of forest for one purpose or another, but so far these fantastic schemes have not been implemented. There is, however, a growing use of these herbicides either as ground or aerial sprays for the elimination of hardwoods and shrubs from some of the forest lands of the country. What this might do to the population of squirrels, raccoons, opossums and other den-loving animals that depend upon forests for food and cover is easily imagined, and there is much concern over this practice. Potentially, it offers equally frightening possibilities as the more spectacular direct kills of birds and animals since, if used successfully over large areas, it may mean the elimination of the best habitat for many kinds of wild creatures. Many of the herbicides are now used to kill out vegetation along power lines, fence rows, and other spots, and by these means further reducing an already inadequate habitat.

These are the major and obvious changes that are affecting farm wildlife. There are other smaller and more local changes that also affect it. Such things as new crops, new crop rotations, new tillage and harvesting practices, and the introduction of new machines may so alter conditions as to benefit some forms and adversely affect others.

There is no easy way to anticipate these changes or to alter their effects. Those interested in wildlife have the opportunity, if constantly alert, to take advantage of those changes that are beneficial and to develop methods that will reduce the harmful effects. In some ways this is one of the most critical problems of wildlife conservation.

8 / Grassland Conservation and Its Relation to Wildlife

Grassland is normally characterized by a perennial cover, but it frequently supports annuals and many other plants than grasses, including broadleaved herbs, both perennial and annual. The character of the vegetation varies with the rainfall and the type of soil.

It has been estimated that grass at one time covered about 40 per cent of the entire land surface of the United States and about half that of the world.

Next to the forest lands, the original grasslands were the most important vegetated areas in this country. Like so much of the land once in virgin forest, they have been extensively abused by injudicious farming and overgrazing.

Disastrous Exploitation for Agriculture

Under the subhumid and semiarid conditions experienced on the Great Plains of the United States, on the low-rainfall sections of the pampas of South America, and on the steppes of Russia, much of the land is unsuited to cultivation. On the remainder, farming is hazardous unless methods are used to conserve the rainfall, and even grazing is a precarious undertaking unless the cover of grass is maintained in stands sufficient to prevent soil blowing. The moist grasslands, on the other hand, such as the prairies of North America and the wetter parts of the pampas of South America, are well suited to the production of wheat, corn, and similar crops.

In the United States the grasslands originally extended north and west from the Gulf coast of Texas across eastern New Mexico and eastern Colorado and northwesterly along the Rockies into Canada. To the south, the approximate eastern boundary was the 98th meridian, and northward the Mississippi River, with easterly extensions across the river, particularly in Wisconsin and Illinois. Farther west there were extensive bodies of grassland over parts of the intermountain areas of northern Idaho, western Wyoming, eastern Oregon and Washington, southern Utah, Arizona, and western New Mexico. The great interior valleys of California also and other scattered areas here and there were predominantly grass covered.

The eastern, better-watered areas were characterized by a growth of tall grasses. Westward, where the rainfall was scantier, short grasses, such as buffalo grass and grama, predominated. In much of the intermountain country the most important were bunch grasses, including a variety of species, such as slender wheat grass and giant wild rye. In many areas where overgrazing and the plow had largely or entirely destroyed the grass, less valuable vegetation has replaced it.

Grassland-Conservation Policies Neglected

Many years ago, when the nation became concerned about the rehabilitation of its cut-over forest lands lying idle and unproductive in large areas, it developed a definite forest-conservation and forest-restoration policy. Equally despoiled, large aggregate areas of grassland have been neglected, and it is only within comparatively recent years that any decided interest has been taken in the problem resulting from improper use of these once valuable lands.

As the white man pushed westward, lured on by the slogan of free land, he took with him a type of agriculture suited to western Europe and the humid eastern United States. This fitted the condi-

Fig. 7 / Generalized map of the Grasslands of North America, shown in black.
(Reprinted by permission from *Our Natural Resources and Their Conservation* by Parkins and Whitaker, published by John Wiley & Sons, Inc., 1936.)

tions fairly well in the high-rainfall or prairie areas, although the running of crop rows up and down slopes instead of along the contours, together with other misapplied practices, resulted in a great deal of soil-impoverishing erosion from the heavy rains. The great problem area was the drier grassland beyond the prairies, that is, on the plains and in the intermountain areas to the west. Despite the wonderful opportunity that existed for the development of a distinctive and profitable type of use for the Plains country, the American people failed to rise to the occasion, although some individuals recognized and pointed out the possibilities. The general rule was to rush in, homestead the land, plow it up, destroy the grass, and plant some kind of crop.

In the more arid parts of the West there did grow up a system of range use that might have developed into a permanent type of land utilization, except for such abuses as overstocking and improper distribution of the herds. The opportunity was handicapped seriously or frustrated outright, however, by the 640-acre homestead law, which apparently was based on the supposition that if a farmer starved out on 160 acres of dry land he ought to make good on 640 acres just as useless for agriculture. If the original settlers had been able to retain control of the lands adjacent to their own large grazing units the drastic overgrazing and destructive erosion that so extensively followed human occupation might have been at least partially avoided.

There was no such control, however, and nomadic stockmen, owning no land and having no interest in the permanency of the land resources or of the grass on it, roamed the country, feeding their animals wherever they could. Pasturing closely and frequently, they quickly depleted large parts of the intermountain ranges. This exploitation of the range was due to a concept of free and unregulated use of the public domain, one of the greatest mistakes in land use ever made by the American people. Large areas were permanently ruined, and the livestock carrying capacity of others was cut to a fraction of what it was originally. It is estimated that much of the range has lost at least half its carrying capacity. Other areas have been even more severely abused.

Unwise Farming Followed by Erosion

In the Great Plains, plowing the grasslands on many millions of acres was followed by accelerated erosion both by wind and by water. It may seem somewhat paradoxical that soils derived from material formed through the action of erosion should have been removed or torn to pieces by the same process. This apparent contradiction can best be understood when it is remembered that land surfaces are constantly being worn down by the slow processes of rock decay, transportation by erosion, and subsequent deposition at lower levels, often in water, again to be transformed into soil and undergo a second cycle of erosion upon exposure of the transported material as land. These geologic processes, as pointed out earlier, have been going on through the ages and are still continuing. Nothing that man can do will greatly alter them.

The extensive vegetative cover stabilized the land in early times and retarded erosion to the tedious process of geologic change. By removing this cover, erosive action was accelerated at a highly destructive rate. Once the top layer of soil with its humus and beneficial microscopic organisms is washed off or blown away, the exposed raw subsoil generally requires long periods of chemical and physical reworking before it can become productive topsoil. If the erosive action goes far enough to remove both soil and subsoil down to bed rock, the whole prolonged geologic process of soil building from parent rock must be repeated before that particular area can again be useful for plant and animal life. In arid regions, soil building goes on more slowly than where more moisture is available for rock disintegration. Where moisture is scanty, vegetative growth is more sparse, decay is slower, and the formation of soil from the broken-down materials takes much longer than under more humid conditions.

Within this century an economic tragedy has been enacted in the comparatively dry country of the Plains states immediately east of the Rockies. In this region, as previously indicated, the precipitation is not sufficient to support the same type of agriculture as in the more humid country to the east. Nevertheless, on millions of acres of Plains country—the loose sandy land as well as the more favorable heavy soils—the native grasses have been plowed out for farming purposes. In years of heavier-than-normal rainfall, success was attained, particularly on the deeper, richer soils, often enough to encourage further settlement. With the gradual decay of the grass roots, however, and exhaustion of the original soil-binding vegetable matter, the soil became looser and more susceptible to wind action. Consequently, under severe drought conditions, the fine particles of sun-parched fields and overgrazed areas have been lifted by the winds and driven across the continent in the great dust storms that were unknown under the virgin conditions of early American settlement. The remaining coarser, less productive particles have been left as dunes and blankets of shifting sand to cover great areas of former grassland. As this is written, this process is still going on; in fact, it is being encouraged by Federal subsidies under inadequate laws and faulty administration.

Possible Economic Uses

Much of this grassland is distinctly submarginal for agriculture. In the average year the less favorable areas do not produce enough crops to sustain a farm population, and in times of drought great suffering spreads across the Plains. Drought, of course, has been largely responsible for the land troubles that have plagued the Plains, and a series of wet years is likely to change the situation. If, however, a vegetative cover is not restored by the heavier precipitation any beneficial effects will be only temporary. On areas without vegetation, the situation will not have been changed, for wind rather than water is there the more destructive agency of erosion.

The only possible economic use for the more severely damaged parts of the Plains is grazing—if and when the grasses are restored. Even on much of the better land the best type of agriculture will be more largely centered around livestock than in the past. To restore grass on the shallow lands and the wind-whipped sandy soils is exceedingly difficult, although it has been demonstrated by the Soil Conservation Service that it can be accomplished slowly by conserving every possible drop of rainfall and adopting contour furrowing, terracing, and other water-saving measures. On the better agricultural lands, fair to good crops can be grown with average rainfall, provided every effort is made to store all water possible in the reservoir of the soil.

Wildlife of the Grasslands

It is not desired to write a program of soil conservation into this book except as it relates to wildlife conservation. Anywhere in areas of low rainfall, however, any effective program for wildlife or for satisfactory human occupancy must be based on adequate conservation of soil and water. The bare drifting sand and the parched soils of abandoned fields are as barren of wildlife as land could well be, and much work remains to be done before anything like a favorable habitat can be reëstablished.

It becomes more obvious with each succeeding drought that soil depletion must be halted if the Plains country is to continue habitable. If this process is checked, conditions will necessarily be improved for wildlife. As a matter of fact, essentially the same thing is true in the humid sections of the East, South, and other parts of the country where soil erosion has taken heavy toll of the productivity of the land. But with the greater supply of moisture in these other regions, it is generally easier to reëstablish some approximation of favorable wildlife habitats than in the Plains or overgrazed sagebrush lands of the West. All these western dry lands once were capable of providing natural vegetation valuable to the human race as well as to the birds and mammals that have an important place in human economy. They can again be restored, but the fact must be faced that in some cases it will be a long and costly undertaking.

The Plains harbored probably the greatest population of large animals that existed anywhere on the North American continent at the time the white man first explored the West. Many estimates have been made as to the numbers of wild animals supported by these grasslands. Some of the figures are interesting, even though they cannot now be verified. The buffalo population of the Great Plains has been estimated at 15,000,000 and upward. In addition, an equal, if not greater, number of antelopes are believed to have inhabitated the region. Seton estimated that there were approximately 10,000,000 elk at the time of the arrival of the first white settlers in the territory now owned by the United States, and it is well known that they ranged the river bottoms from the Mississippi westward throughout the Plains. Deer and smaller game also abounded.

Buffalo

In their prime the buffalo herds constituted one of the greatest aggregations of a single species of large animal occupying an equal area anywhere on earth and, together with the deer, elk, and antelope, undoubtedly made one of the greatest concentrated herds of hoofed animals that has existed within historic times. Now that the buffalo herds are largely gone, the nation has little to show for their passing. They were wasted, heedlessly—killed by the thousands for the fun of killing or solely for their hides. Even when they were slaughtered for food, only the choicest parts of the carcasses were utilized, so abundant and unfailing was the supply considered. With them have gone most of the other larger wild animals of the Plains. From the big-game standpoint, the region is one of the poorest in North America.

Except for herds on reservations, the buffalo has vanished from the United States proper. There is one free herd in the Wood Buffalo National Park, Canada. The only truly wild stock remaining in the possession of the United States originated from a small herd that was planted along the Big Delta River, near Fairbanks, Alaska, and that now numbers about 255 based on an aerial survey made in November, 1955. In recent years on the Crow Reservation in Montana the Indians have planted surplus buffaloes furnished by the National Park Service and the U. S. Fish and Wildlife Service and are trying to develop a herd there.

Small herds are scattered in various parts of the United States outside the national parks and the big-game refuges of the U. S. Fish and Wildlife Service. The chief public herds in this country are found on the National Bison Range, Montana, Wichita Mountains

Wildlife Refuge, Oklahoma, and Fort Niobrara Game Preserve, Nebraska, controlled by the U. S. Fish and Wildlife Service and on Yellowstone National Park, Wyoming, and Wind Cave National Park, South Dakota.

Antelope

The antelope has fared somewhat better than has the buffalo, though in about 1920 the species reached its lowest ebb. At that time homesteading and the breaking up of the ranges had progressed to a peak. A series of wet years in the intermountain country, where the last great herds survived, stimulated homesteading to such an extent that little room was left for the animals, and it seemed as if the species might perish. For example, many dry valleys in eastern Oregon—Catlow Valley, Fort Rock, and Christmas Lake among others—were homesteaded from about 1910 to 1915. For a while they produced fair crops of rye, barley, and other grains and vegetation. Later, a period of decreased rainfall drove out the homesteaders. Now comparatively few inhabitants are left and little farming is carried on in these valleys. Many towns and communities of the period are entirely deserted. Much of the land has been overgrazed by sheep and cattle and is in poor condition. Nevertheless, some food is left for the antelope. Scattered bands, some of them kept alive through the interest of a few livestock operators, were available for breeding stock when the recession of settlement began.

As the settlers moved out of the country, the antelope increased and spread until now six times as many occupy the region as there were at that time. In 1924, E. W. Nelson estimated as the result of a careful survey that only about 30,000 of these beautiful desert animals were left in the United States. At present there are in this country certainly between 190,000 and 200,000. Wyoming, Oregon, Nevada, Arizona, New Mexico, Montana, Idaho, and South Dakota have thriving herds. In terms of numbers taken by hunters, the pronghorn has outstripped the deer in importance in recent hunting seasons in Wyoming; the 1954 hunter harvest in that state alone nearly equalled the total numbers of all antelope existing in the United States in 1920! Texas, Colorado, and Nebraska have small remaining populations from which stocks are being built up under improved grasslands conditions.

Elk, Deer, and Other Game

The elk, of course, is entirely gone from the prairies, plains, and other open grasslands; deer also have been wiped out except for scattering small herds. Prairie chickens and sharptailed grouse, particularly the former, have been largely extirpated over most of the grassland, although scattered birds are left here and there through their original range.

Uncompensated Loss of Wildlife

Perhaps this depletion of wildlife might be accepted with less perturbation if there had been a corresponding increase in human values. Unfortunately, there has been no such compensation. As vegetation and wildlife vanished, so went the savings of thousands of farmers who hopefully settled in the western grasslands. As a result of the misguided enthusiasm of many such settlers, the nation now faces the gigantic problem of restoring to some kind of productive use millions of acres of formerly well-grassed country. Inasmuch as the best possible economic use for a vast aggregate area of the misused and less favorable parts of the original grass country is grazing, either these lands should be restored as speedily as possible to grass or some type of agriculture that is built around grass should be developed.

Correcting Past Mistakes

Gloomy predictions have been made that it will take 20 to 100 years to restore perennial grasses to the misused Plains country. This may be true for some of the drier sections and the more sandy and shallower soils, but accumulating evidence indicates that the process can be greatly accelerated. Much will depend on the stage of depletion. Bare soil, moving under the impact of wind, can never be stabilized until enough vegetation is established to slow down the movement to a static or nearly static condition. This frequently will require even the planting of weeds as a first step toward grass recovery. Other thousands of acres can be stabilized within a reasonable time only if adequate measures are taken to conserve as much as possible of the rainfall, such as contour furrowing, contour listing, and water spreading. Some land can be reclothed with grass eventually simply by taking off all stock and keeping it off until the growth is sufficient to hold the soil. Even with such cover reëstablished, subsequent grazing must be so controlled that the plants will not again disappear faster than they can be reproduced.

Soil drifting can be minimized or controlled in many localities by strip cropping, that is, by planting the taller crops, as Sudan grass or corn, between those that are lower growing. Wherever farming is carried on, another good soil-holding practice is to preserve as much as possible of all crop residues and stubbles.

The task of correcting past mistakes in the utilization of the western grasslands constitutes a problem of enormous proportions and one intimately related to our future national welfare. Probably the most feasible solution of the problem as it relates to large areas is to bring the poorer lands into public ownership, restore them to grass, and then permit grazing under adequate restrictions for the good of the land and the dependent communities.

In the chapter on forest conservation, the stabilization of communities by sustained-yield forestry practices was discussed. In handling the grasslands the same objectives must somehow be attained if future economic values commensurate with their possibilities are to be assured. The best possible use for much of this land, as already noted, is the production of grass and the development of communities based on its proper utilization. Throughout this vast area of the Great Plains are many thousands of acres that, with proper methods, can be satisfactorily farmed. Such farming can and should be integrated with the wise use of the grasses. After restoration, such grasslands can have both recreational and economic values if they carry also an increased stock of wildlife.

Wildlife Restoration

With proper foresight, the great buffalo herds that once roamed the Plains might easily have been preserved in limited numbers and levied on to provide tremendous quantities of meat annually, without appreciable depletion of the supply. Now these magnificent animals are gone from the Plains never to return, though under conditions of public ownership and management it may not be an entirely fantastic dream to visualize the reëstablishment of scattered herds within the bounds of their ancestral home.

With the grass restored and properly used, smaller game and nongame animals also can easily be restored in moderate numbers over much of the land. Antelopes have demonstrated their recuperative ability and many have come back, even in the face of adverse conditions. Deer have been restored to some of the Badlands of the Dakotas, Wyoming, and Montana, and in similar areas where food and shelter are available.

The Charles Sheldon Antelope Refuge in northern Nevada may be cited as an example of partial restoration of wildlife in the overused or misused grassland country. An area of approximately 30,000 acres was purchased and established as a wildlife refuge in 1931 with money contributed by the National Association of Audubon Societies and the Boone and Crockett Club of New York. In succeeding years sheep were kept off, but without fencing it was impossible to exclude cattle and horses. The refuge was given to the Biological Survey (now known as the U.S. Fish and Wildlife Service) for administration on August 5, 1932, but it was not until two years later that funds became available to surround it with a fence that would exclude horses and cattle but allow antelopes to go in and out. When the fence was sufficiently near completion to keep out livestock, the areas around the waterholes were entirely bare of vegetation and the sagebrush slopes were denuded of grass to the point of barrenness. Even the sagebrush itself had been browsed until it was stunted and scattered. Aspen thickets on the hillsides had been browsed by livestock until they were in a dying condition, and for many years no young plants survived to take their place.

In the two years between August 1934 and August 1936 the appearance of the refuge entirely changed. Plots around the waterholes were covered with clumps of rye grass that stood shoulder-high. All through the sagebrush, bunch grass came back in scattered clumps —not a perfect stand by any means, but it was knee-high—and other vegetation was springing up. The browse plants made a good growth, and young aspens stood through the seasons, starting the replacement of the clumps that had been killed or stunted from too heavy browsing. The contrast between conditions before and after fencing was amazing: the recovery was far beyond anything anticipated by those directing it. This experience indicates that if the plants have a chance to reseed themselves, ranges that are not entirely destroyed can come back very quickly.

The value of this refuge was enhanced in 1936 by the addition of nearly 500,000 acres of outside land, which, under restricted grazing, will be available for winter range for the antelope. Most of the private land included within those half a million acres has been purchased and will be devoted to the production and perpetuation of wildlife. The Charles Sheldon Refuge should preserve not only many antelopes and mule deer, but also sage hens, magnificent game birds of the western country. All three still inhabit the area and the adjacent Hart Mountain Antelope Refuge of 270,000 acres just to the north in Oregon which also was established in 1936.

It is the belief of a number of biologists that the greatest success with wildlife rehabilitation in the Plains country can be attained by restoring native vegetation. The buffalo grass and the grama of the short-grass country have been adapted through centuries to dry conditions. They survived because of their ability to withstand the vicissitudes of life under the prevailing climatic and soil conditions. It seems probable, therefore, that they will be more successful in rehabilitating the range than any foreign plants that might be introduced.

The grassland-restoration program should go hand in hand with a definite program for the restoration of wildlife. Like the native grasses, the native species of wildlife, though crowded out or reduced in numbers, probably will do better than could any introduced birds or animals. Deer and antelopes in some localities and the smaller inhabitants of the grasslands certainly can be restored in numbers. The list includes some of the fur animals as well as upland birds, both game and nongame.

As the conditions in the Great Plains are improved, so also will be the surface water conditions. Many of the lakes and marshes have dried up by drainage and cultivation, particularly in the Dakotas, western Minnesota, and northern Nebraska. Not only were these lakes and marshes once valuable for wildlife production, but they also contributed to the maintenance of the water level and the originally luxuriant crops of native grasses. The eastern part of the grassland area, that is, the prairies, will probably never be restored to grass. This region has proved to be generally a good agricultural country and is undoubtedly more valuable for that purpose than for any other.

For much of the land between the 98th meridian and the eastern slopes of the Cascade Range of the Sierra Nevada, grass is the most important possible crop. Not only will it help the native wildlife, but the restoration of thickets of berry-bearing shrubs and trees in damp spots and sheltered ravines will be of major importance in supplementing the cover and winter food upon which many birds and mammals are dependent in time of climatic emergency. The wild plum, wild cherry, snowberry, coralberry, elderberry, juniper, sumac, and many other widely distributed plants that are usually found in patches add greatly to wildlife values. The restoration of lakes and marshes should go hand in hand with the improvement or rehabilitation of grasslands. Not only will these marshes produce many valuable plants but they will also furnish water for all forms of wildlife and domestic stock and in addition yield a supply of game and fishes and a crop of fur animals. Maintaining them will restore water tables and provide a water supply against emergencies. Destruction of lakes and marshes was one of the most disastrous mistakes ever made in this country, particularly in the semiarid region, where they served an even more useful purpose than in the more humid areas eastward.

Scattered throughout the grassland country are a number of wildlife refuges of various types. The U.S. Fish and Wildlife Service has reëstablished native grasses and other vegetation on the upland parts of some refuges under its control. These areas can be made productive, and under careful administration it is hoped that each will serve as a nucleus for a general restoration of native vegetation and wildlife.

Many of the prairie refuges harbor sharp-tailed grouse and prairie chickens. There are as many more on which small colonies of sage hens and antelopes are present, in addition to the two special antelope ranges in northern Nevada and southern Oregon. Wildlife restoration, based on sound biological principles, is thus found to be closely correlated with the sound conservation of the grasslands.

Restoration a Federal Problem

The restoration of grassland constitutes one of the greatest conservation problems before the American public today. Making these ranges more productive involves sound management operations on an area equal to two-fifths of the land surface of the United States. To the extent that they are successful the grasslands will become areas supporting stabilized communities dependent for their livelihood upon grass and its products, and at the same time the vanishing and nearly vanished types of wildlife will not only be preserved but increased in numbers. No one can entirely foresee the future values of these wildlife resources, either from a recreational or a monetary standpoint.

In the years following the drought of the 1930's there was considerable progress in developing and applying new land management techniques to the denuded and blowing grasslands known then as the "Dust Bowl." However, following the outbreak of the second World War, the stimulus of high prices and later a fantastic high price support program much land was replowed and greater areas of grassland were broken up.

Apparently the lesson of the 1930's was largely lost and the nation paid, and is still paying, the bill for this short-sighted policy. It paid first to stimulate this destruction of the grassland, and when the inevitable dry years returned, it paid for disaster relief through various Federal subsidies and grants on lands that never should have been plowed.

Following this there has been new interest in the grassland problem. Steps toward new agricultural legislation have been taken, and the conservation reserve section of the Soil Bank legislation may possibly have a beneficial effect on grassland restoration.

9 / Some Basic Facts in Wildlife Conservation

The previous chapters, in dealing with general conservation, have attempted to show the interrelationships between the conservation of wildlife and the conservation of soil, water, forests, and grasslands. In the present chapter there are enumerated and defined certain general facts and principles that bear directly upon wildlife conservation. Only a few of the more important basic biological concepts are mentioned here, as the limitations of space alone forbid going into intricate biological details that even trained workers find difficult to value properly.

The aphorism that "nature abhors a vacuum" expresses a biological truth, for every livable place has life. Each unit of land and water tends to produce its own quota of living things. The quantity and type of life vary greatly, depending upon the food and cover available, the temperature, and other factors. It is not necessary to discuss these factors in detail or their relative importance to living things, for every person can recall illustrations from his own observation. For instance, he will have seen a fallow field or a new road grade quickly covered with weeds, or a newly created pond almost immediately inhabited by numerous forms of plant and animal life.

On every acre of land there is a teeming community of plants and animals, varying from the simpler forms that live in the soil through numerous more advanced groups of the plant and animal kingdoms. All have a rôle to play in maintaining the biotic community; in fact the soil bacteria, the protozoans, and the lowly earthworms may in the aggregate be more productive, and thus basically more important, than the conspicuous birds and mammals of the surface.

Ecology

The study of biotic communities and of the associations and interrelationships between living things is called ecology. As a jibe at the penchant of certain ecologists for creating long words to describe familiar things, ecology was once defined as "elaboration of the obvious in terms that no one can understand." Many things in ecology *are* obvious. The existence of living communities, and their arrangement in colonies and associations can be seen by everyone. When, however, an attempt is made to find the reasons for particular combinations, and to understand the relationships of the component species and why the succession of forms lives on a given acre of land or water, ecology does indeed become complex.

For many years biology was chiefly concerned with the sorting, classifying, and naming of plants and animals—a tremendous task and one by no means complete. Other phases of biology are now receiving more attention—among them ecology, or the study of populations of plants and animals and their interrelationships. This broad science seeks to understand the make-up of populations and the tensions and adjustments that exist within them. It is a living, dynamic sort of biology that may prove to be of major import to human communities and nations.

Through the ages "climax," or relatively stable, types of vegetation have developed in response to the principal phases of soil and climate. The "climax type" simply means a plant, or combination of plants, so well suited to a certain soil, climate, and set of growing conditions that once established it tends to maintain itself. By this special term are designated such familiar things as hardwood or pine forests, bunchgrass or short-grass prairies, and other associations.

Where disturbances by man or where great natural changes do not interfere, such plant communities tend to persist for long periods. Associated with them are a great variety of insects, birds, and mammals, to mention only a few of the widely known types of living things that are able to live directly or indirectly on the plant products of the climax.

Ecological communities vary as a whole or in detail. The aggregation of living matter produced on a given area changes with each growing season. For instance, a year of severe drought may greatly decrease the production of plant food. Lacking a dependable supply of that food, animals may die of starvation or be the victims of other chains of events originating in the shortage of food. Reduction in animal life may, in turn, have effects on the plant growth the following season. This is a simple case; others much more complicated though less obvious are in process all the time.

Variation in community detail may be illustrated by a change in relationships between species. Such changes are constantly occurring. Sometimes the causes and effects are obvious; at other times they are obscure. A cold, wet spring may result in such a poor reproduction of ground-nesting birds and burrowing animals that in the following breeding season there will be a scantier population than usual of these species. A more luxuriant production of grass, herbage, and shrubbery the same year may conceivably result in better food and cover conditions for the grazing species. Hence there might be an increased survival of big game at the time some birds and burrowing animals were depleted. A single factor may thus simultaneously react favorably on some animal populations and unfavorably on others. Its consequences may affect other species and cause such changes in numerical relationships as to modify the community for several years. Sometimes, especially in population fluctuations, the results are obvious, though the causes may be obscure. For example, hunters have learned that there may be good and poor supplies of game in succeeding years, but they may never fully comprehend the complex chains of events that cause these variations.

Man Changes Climax Types

When a climax type of vegetation is disrupted, as it often is locally, great changes in the entire animal population follow. It makes no difference whether the change is due to man or to nature, the result will be the same. A great landslide removing the soil and forest from a mountainside not only carries away the animal life but renders the area unfit for a similar animal association for many years to come. Floods, lightning fires, volcanic eruptions, earthquakes, and other natural phenomena may drastically alter the biological community.

Man also can and does alter animal communities as he goes about remaking the face of the earth to suit his notions or needs. He cuts down the forest, and immediately the animal life dependent on the woodland must move on or perish. He plows the grasslands, and the same alternatives confront their animal populations. When he drains the marshes and lakes, the marsh birds fly elsewhere and the aquatic life dies.

Climax types, however, being particularly suited to their respective conditions, tend to come back. Cut-over forest land as a rule returns to forest; plowed-up grassland to grass. Disturbed areas sometimes revert directly to the climax type, but sometimes only through a succession of stages. A drained area may again fill with water if the ditches become clogged; and return of the water may be followed by marsh, lake, and aquatic vegetation that gradually conforms to the original type. When man attempts to use cut-over forest lands for other purposes he may have difficulty in preventing reëstablishment of the forest. In the tropics, for example, a jungle quickly invades artificial clearings unless constant vigilance is maintained. In temperate regions, natural reforestation is less rapid but none the less certain on unplowed lands. In many areas where soil, climate and moisture favor forest growth, old fields and pastures quickly come up to pine, cedar, birch or other woodland types.

Where climax forest is destroyed, certain events follow in a more or less regular way—a process known as succession. A fire, sufficiently hot to destroy the trees, leaves a blackened scar on the landscape. Yet the ground is soon clothed with vegetation—not forest, but mosses, ferns, and annual flowering plants, the spores and seeds of which are light enough to be carried by the wind. Perennial herbs, shrubs, and trees come in more slowly. Finally, a growing forest may again occupy the burn. The animal life as well as the plant growth shows stages in succession resulting from changes in composition, some species disappearing and others replacing them or the same species remaining but varying greatly in the proportional numbers present. Such changes are natural biological responses to alteration in vegetative cover, whether as a result of natural events or of man's efforts.

Effects of Exotic Species

When man settles in a new land he not only changes the climax type of vegetation but also brings to it strange plants and animals. Some of these are introduced deliberately, others unwittingly. Crop and garden plants and domestic animals are sure to be brought with him as well as some kinds of game, and less frequently species of esthetic interest. In addition, parasites and predators may be deliberately imported for use in biological control, especially of insects, and unintentionally species arrive that become serious pests, including weeds, injurious insects, rats, and mice.

The introduction of exotic species is a complicated subject and deserves much more consideration than has been accorded it. Biologists almost universally feel that it is unwise to introduce a foreign species for liberation in the wild. Their feeling is based somewhat on a sentimental objection to mixing a foreign element with the native flora and fauna, but to a greater extent on the unpredictable and often unfavorable biological and economic effects of such importations.

If geological history is correctly interpreted, however, the first objection is to some extent academic. New forms have been invading new territories and still are constantly doing so; and as conditions have changed, entire floras and faunas have been crowded out, a change which may again occur. The second is a valid objection, and because of the unfavorable results introduction is strictly regulated or even prohibited by many countries.

Occasionally even deliberately introduced species find conditions very much to their liking and become so abundant as to affect man's interests adversely. The European rabbit in Australia, the North American muskrat in Europe, and the English sparrow and the European starling in the United States are among species that have caused trouble not anticipated by those responsible for introducing them.

To replace depleted native forms, foreign game birds and, to a lesser extent, foreign mammals have been widely introduced. Much money, time, and effort have been expended to find species that will maintain themselves better in an environment modified by man than have the native forms. Most of the attempts have resulted in failure. In this country the only three introduced game species that now, after years of effort, are numerous enough to be hunted for sport to any considerable extent are the ring-necked pheasant, the Hungarian partridge, and the chukar partridge.

Crop and garden plants sometimes invade other than cultivated lands and become naturalized. Weed seeds introduced with those of cultivated plants, or accidentally in other commerce, are widely distributed. Exotic insects in constantly increasing numbers also have established themselves in this country. Many more are introduced than survive, but occasionally a newcomer finds conditions so much to its liking that it spreads rapidly and, through absence of the competitive species with which it had to contend in its original home and unharassed by its normal parasites and predators, it becomes much more seriously harmful to man's interests. Insects have been most conspicuous in this respect, and the searching out, importation, and establishment of the parasites of these alien invaders has become a standard method of control.

Plants and Animals in Human Economy

Wildlife affects man and his interests in many ways, and his policy toward animals is influenced by their relationships to him. His reaction toward wildlife may be based either on accurate facts or on faulty data, and in some cases even on tradition or superstition. He recognizes his dependence on the plant and animal world for food, clothing, and numerous other things. Though he now enjoys cultivated crops and meat and other products of domestic animals, a more primitive society depended upon wild fruits, seeds, plant fibers and the returns from the chase. Considerations of cultivated and domestic forms belong to an agricultural treatise, not here; but a discussion of man's relationships to the uncultivated and untamed forms about him is properly in the field of a work on the conservation of natural resources.

It is to be first emphasized, however, that from the purely biological point of view there are no beneficial and no harmful plants or animals. All are cogs long fitted in the great biological mechanism, one having its function as well as another. The rattlesnake has its place as much as has the oriole; the worm does its turn in the drama of life as worthily as does the deer. All play their parts also in the complex natural process that builds soils and maintains their fertility. As the fertility increases, so does the vegetative production, and completing the cycle, there is more food for animal forms, and so on through the endless chain of life. By the total machinery of nature the fertile soils our predecessors found on this continent were built, and it is by that mechanism, and so far as known, by that alone, that they can be maintained. It is therefore vitally necessary to man's interests that the natural process be kept at work by allowing communities of plant and animal life to exist and thrive on every bit of land not needed for any other purpose.

Man's classification of animals and plants into beneficial or injurious is not therefore fundamentally biological, but usually economic and occasionally esthetic. On this basis, species are classified according to their real or supposed effects on man's interests. The beneficial wild animals are thus roughly divisible into game forms that furnish sport and incidentally food; fishes, particularly those good for food, including for economic purposes clams, oysters, crabs, and other water forms; fur animals that provide valuable pelts; species that feed on others more destructive to man's interests (that is, birds that feed on insects); and species valued for the esthetic pleasure they bring through beauty of form, song, or interesting ways. Plants that are economically valuable include trees that furnish lumber, fruits, and nuts; plants whose roots, seeds, or other parts are gathered for food; grasses that are valuable for pasturing domestic animals or useful as sources of usable fibers; and a variety of others.

Species generally classified as injurious are the weeds that invade man's cultivated fields and pasture lands and the animals that feed on his crops or livestock or that prey on the wild species that he considers valuable. Two facts that should be clearly understood at this point are: (1) that there is no general agreement as to these classifications; and (2) that species classed as pests have certain characteristics in common.

Different groups of men may consider the same species either beneficial or injurious as it affects, or appears to affect, their own immediate interests. Fox hunters deem the fox a valuable species, but the poultryman and the quail hunter regard it injurious. To the poultryman and gamekeeper, minks and skunks may be pests; to the trapper and fur trader, however, they provide the basis for one of our oldest industries, for when taken at the proper season their furs bring large monetary return. Truck gardeners and farmers often regard the introduced ring-necked pheasant as destructive, while gunners in the same community prize it as a game species. Those who enjoy the beauty of bird life appreciate the herons, while fishermen object to their presence. There also are often differences of opinion among those with an esthetic interest in particular groups. For example, persons interested only in birds dislike and often persecute the red squirrel because of its depredations on bird nests; those interested in mammals encourage the chickaree and enjoy its interesting and impudent manners. Even wildlife managers interested chiefly in game frequently are oblivious of the fact that management must be applied also to the fur resources.

These examples would indicate that man's artificial classification of wildlife on the basis of self-interest is subject to other interpretations in the light of individual or group interests. Moreover, when the fact is remembered that his classifications are often based on incomplete or erroneous information, the complexity of wildlife policies becomes painfully apparent.

The various injurious weeds, crop-destroying animals, and the stock predators all have two characteristics in common—fecundity and adaptability. Those plants that invade our fields as the worst weeds are able to grow under a wide variety of conditions, and they produce quantities of seed or propagate rapidly by underground runners or other vegetative methods. The very characters that make them biologically successful do the most to bring them into conflict with man's interests.

Among the annual weeds, purslane, ragweed, lambsquarters, and many others have habits of growth and seeding and tolerances that fit well into the cultural practices necessary to grow many crops; thus they are able to succeed where other plants cannot. Some of the worst perennial weeds are those with underground rootstalks that have vitality enough for every section to grow when broken or cut off from the parent plant. Man's necessary tillage of crops thus often aids the rapid spread of plants entirely undesirable from his point of view.

Similarly an animal or bird that becomes a pest is one that can adapt itself to the changed conditions brought about by man and can readily substitute cultivated crops or domestic animals for its former natural foods often largely suppressed by man's operations.

Utilization of Wild Species

When man utilizes a wild species for game, food, or commercial purposes, that species is immediately subjected to a pressure that adds to its difficulties in maintaining existence. The added pressure varies in intensity with the number of its pursuers and with the methods used in taking it, but the ultimate effect is often greatly to reduce the population of the game or food species not only in comparison with other forms but also in total numbers.

To compensate for this added pressure man often attempts to remove other pressures (e.g., he kills natural enemies), undertakes artificial restocking (planting fish or game species), resorts to artificial feeding at critical times, or tries to improve conditions for the favored species. Sometimes these efforts have a sound basis and are more or less successful; often the reverse is true. The significant thing is that attempts have been made, and are today being made on an increasing scale, to maintain and, if possible, increase species regarded as beneficial and to suppress those classed as injurious. These efforts have led to the development of a new profession and a new art in this country, namely that of wildlife management.

Wildlife Management

The very term "wildlife management" carries recognition of the importance of many of the things mentioned in preceding paragraphs. It recognizes the reality and operation of ecological communities and that man's activities often greatly disturb them; thence that it is often desirable from the human viewpoint to work with these communities and attempt to modify or manage them in man's interests.

The primitive conditions of the America of 1500 cannot be restored; that is beyond human power, but even if it were possible, few would favor it. This country could again become a land of the prevailing climaxes of vegetation and their associated animal life only if man ceased tilling the soil, polluting the waters, draining the marshes, and damming the streams. Such a primitive land could support only the scant human population that could live on wild plant products and the spoils of the chase. As soon as any greater population began to utilize the forests and till the lands all the

THE BOBWHITE IS A POPULAR RESIDENT

Plate 17 / If cover and food conditions are adequate (above), the bobwhite quail (below) not only nests in but also inhabits the same general locality throughout the year.

(Fish and Wildlife Service photos: B47446 by W. P. Taylor; B6M by W. D. Gay.)

PELICANS AND TERNS NEST IN COLONIES

Plate 18 / **White pelicans and robal terns, both migrant birds, find protection fo their nesting colonies on Federal refuges—the former on the Clear Lake National Wild life Refuge in California (above) and the latter on Cape Romain Refuge in Nort Carolina (below).**

(Fish and Wildlife Service photos: B40470 by Ira N. Gabrielson; B7108M by W. F Kubichek.)

BIRDS CANNOT NEST ON THE WING

Plate 19 / Restoring areas to provide nesting places for migratory birds like the Canada goose (above) on the Crescent Lake National Wildlife Refuge in Nebraska is part of the Federal wildlife program; a once-drained area when developed into the Lower Souris Refuge in North Dakota produced its first family of Canada geese in 25 years (below).

(Fish and Wildlife Service photos: B51639 by E. R. Kalmbach; B50835 by C. J. Henry.)

ONLY DUCKS CAN PRODUCE DUCKS

Plate 20 / Broods of ducklings like the pintails and Barrow's goldeneyes (above) can be produced only if nesting places like that used by the black duck (below) are preserved and an adequate stock of adult birds is returned to the breeding grounds.

(Fish and Wildlife Service photos: 2597s, photographer unknown; B38359 by Olaus J. Murie; B37620 by O. L. Austin, Jr.; B48795a by Paul D. Dalke.)

THE DOVE ESCAPED THE PIGEON'S FATE

Plate 21 / **Unlike the extinct, colony-nesting passenger pigeon whose fate it escaped, the mourning dove, a game bird as well as a songbird, raises its young (below) in solitary nesting places; doves are now protected under the Migratory Bird Treaty Act.**

(Fish and Wildlife Service photos: B947M by Ira N. Gabrielson; B57936 by Allen M. Pearson.)

WILDLIFE'S BEAUTY CAN BE BOTH HAZARDOUS AND PROTECTIVE

Plate 22 / Once threatened with extermination by hunters seeking beautiful plumes, the American egrets (above and below) and other plumage birds have been successfully protected as a result of efforts to perpetuate their beauty.

(Fish and Wildlife Service photos: B44502 by John Boswell; 2746s, photographer unknown.)

LONG LEGS DO NOT ALWAYS MEAN NECKS AS LONG

Plate 23 / Although nearly every long-legged bird, like the sandhill crane (below), has a neck about as long as its legs, the black-necked stilt, a shorebird with long legs (above), has a comparatively short neck yet reaches its food easily by bending its knees with agility.

(Fish and Wildlife Service photos: B6412M by S. A. Grimes; B124X2 by Howard Zahniser.)

SMALL BIRDS HAVE GREAT FRIENDS

Plate 24 / Thousands of bird lovers each winter provide hand-outs for such small birds as the black-capped chickadee (above) and each spring welcome such nesting birds as the catbird (below).

(Fish and Wildlife Service photos: B1332M, photographer unknown; B31547 by E. R. Kalmbach.)

ecological changes outlined in this chapter would inevitably ensue. It is doubtless true that if with present-day knowledge this nation could begin again with the America of 400 years ago, it could do a better job of handling the soils, waters, and forests, and the wildlife. It would be possible to utilize the resources freely without wrecking the machinery as has been done. It is useless, however, to decry past mistakes except with the aim of avoiding similar errors in the future. The job now is to repair the damage so far as possible and put natural constructive processes back to work. The new art of wildlife management, the new attacks on soil erosion, and the improved programs of reforestation and water conservation are the result of a growing understanding of the necessity of these processes for human welfare.

Wildlife management, like other conservation measures, has an important part to play but insists that it build upon the firm foundation of a constantly increasing body of facts about the complex relationships among living things. Accurate knowledge must replace theories and traditions. In the light of present knowledge, management can deal with only one, or at most a few, species on a given piece of land and closely watch and interpret the results. From such efforts, however, will gradually evolve the much-needed technique of general ecological management. In its present state, wildlife management is an effort to apply to urgent problems the ecological and biological data that are now available, always with the consciousness that existing tools, methods, and processes may have to be discarded as new and better information becomes available.

In succeeding chapters some of the problems and difficulties in dealing with wildlife will be outlined. Since management is developing according to the varied relationships between wildlife and man, it will be discussed from that standpoint. To be constantly kept in mind, however, is the thought that this classification of animals is controlled by man's interests and is not made on a biological basis.

10 / Resident Game

Among the most significant of the many factors that influence resident game and other wildlife populations are availability of food supplies, presence of suitable cover, abundance and effectiveness of predatory species, competition with other species or with domestic stock, and disease. The interplay of these and various other factors of minor importance is often intricate and difficult to understand.

The needs of the forms of resident wildlife considered as game may vary in detail according to species and locality, but the basic requirements for both mammals and birds are the same. Suitable environment must be present, and by that is meant food, cover, and other habitat adequate to meet the year-long needs. Where such necessities exist in proper relationship it is possible not only to conserve but to increase existing stocks or to reintroduce depleted species successfully, provided the take by man is sufficiently controlled.

In the present discussion of the basic philosophy of restoring and conserving wildlife no attempt can be made to include all these factors. Consideration must be limited rather to those that, with our present knowledge, we can modify in the interests of wildlife.

Food and cover, the most important of these, can be influenced if the requirements of the species to be favored are first known. Such changes as can be effected for the advantage of one form, however, may be to the disadvantage of others. To be of the greatest value without doing harm, therefore, changes must be fully considered and measures carefully applied.

Predation, a factor of less importance, but one that can be affected by man's activities, will be discussed in a separate chapter. Another consideration, and one entirely controllable by man, is concerned with the annual harvest: to maintain game in a given territory the harvest must be restricted to the surplus available above the necessary breeding stock.

Influence of Local Conditions

Application of the basic principles for maintaining game is often made difficult by local conditions or by lack of understanding of these conditions. In some instances it is further complicated by the fact that the breeding stock has been reduced to such a low level that the very existence of a species is threatened despite the establishment of an entirely closed season, intended, so far as possible, to prevent human interference. An extreme depletion may simplify decisions as to imposing restrictions on the annual harvest, but it may also magnify the importance of adverse factors, such as predation, that would ordinarily be of little consequence to normal populations.

It is gratifying to note that it is possible for those controlling a relatively small area to provide suitable year-long conditions for resident game species and maintain huntable surpluses regardless of what neighbors may do. In Texas there are single ranches that sustain good populations of deer and turkeys; in the Southwest there are quail-shooting preserves that are successfully managed by one or a few individuals; and in Ohio there are township and county associations that by coöperative efforts have built up the densest pheasant populations to be found in this country.

The fact that resident game is limited in its range has resulted in a phenomenal growth in the development of private shooting preserves on which birds may be hunted for a fee. The first of these areas was established in Michigan in 1929, but the great majority of states now have legislation permitting such establishments. Ring-necked pheasants are the type of game most frequently offered for controlled shooting, but mallards, quail, and in a few places deer and turkey are offered on a limited basis. The greatest concentration of such preserves is, as would be expected, relatively close to large centers of population, but a growing number are somewhat farther afield.

Resident game species are more easily handled than are migratory waterfowl, whose breeding ranges and winter homes may be a thousand miles or more apart. It is difficult to provide uniform treatment for these visitors to many areas, particularly when resident hunters and game managers may hold divergent views regarding the needs of the birds and the methods of supplying these needs. Whether migratory or resident, however, the continued existence of game in sufficient numbers to afford hunting is dependent on recognition of its requirements for abundant survival and on meeting these requirements by suitable game- and land-management practices.

Resident game problems fall rather naturally into three groups, according to the following classification of the birds or mammals involved:

1. Browsing and grazing big game, including deer, elk, moose, bighorn sheep, mountain goats, antelopes, and caribous.
2. Small game, as quails, grouse, turkeys, rabbits, and squirrels.
3. Miscellaneous forms variably classed as game, predators, or fur animals, as for example, raccoons, foxes, and bears. To avoid duplication, the species in this group will be discussed in the chapter on fur animals.

Deer and Elk

The big-game resources of this country present some of the most perplexing problems of management that confront those who would manage wildlife. As dire consequences, for instance, can menace a species through overabundance as through allowing too much hunting.

Not many years ago it was generally believed by those interested in deer that the only thing needed to conserve those noble animals was to provide them with refuges and let nature take its course. So long as the populations were low this theory worked beautifully. Pennsylvania, as an example, starting with practically no deer, imported and released 1,192 animals in the years between 1906 and 1925. Under the favorable food conditions created by the logging of original forests, this basic stock, protected by widely distributed refuges, an adequate patrol backed by public opinion, and an increasing food supply as the forests grew back, increased into one of the finest deer herds in America. From the restorationist's point of view it was a fine job. But the deer did not stop increasing; they went on and on, overbrowsed the forage, and brought starvation upon themselves—creating a new set of problems as perplexing as the former scarcity of deer had been distressing.

The Kaibab deer herd, already mentioned built up to huge numbers by protection on a great natural range, is not only a classic example of the success of refuges in increasing animal populations but also of the deplorable results of overpopulation.

These and other instances have proven the fact that every area is definitely limited in its capacity to produce big game. The animals can and do increase to the point where they not only consume all the available food but also browse the plants so severely as to limit progressively their productiveness in succeeding seasons. On the Kaibab, for example, the deer herd became so large that it not only ate up the seasonal growth but actually killed great quantities of the better browse plants. That example demonstrated that it is just as possible to overgraze a big-game area as a livestock pasturage and the results are equally disastrous. General recognition of this fact is one of the definite advances in wildlife management in recent years. A good farmer or stockman who wants to stay in business cannot allow his pastures to be overgrazed to the point of starving his breeding stock; neither can the wildlife manager.

To hold animal populations to the number that can be supported on particular areas involved would not seem difficult, but in practice the problem is often complicated. In many areas having an abundance of summer food but a great shortage of winter forage, this condition alone has prevented the success of numerous efforts at restocking that were otherwise sound.

In western states the mountains are great reservoirs for the deer and elk populations that provide big-game hunting. Usually there is ample summer food for even greater herds than now exist, but the former winter ranges in the foothills and lower valleys are now occupied by farms and stock ranches, and the available food is appropriated to other uses. Under these conditions game managers must either provide more winter ranges or limit the numbers of big game. They are attempting to achieve their objectives in both ways, first by buying up tracts of major importance for wintering grounds, and then by so regulating the hunting as to reduce herds whose population pressure has reached the danger point.

An illustration of winter-range acquisition is furnished by the National Elk Refuge in Jackson Hole, Wyoming. There, 18,000 acres have been purchased to provide winter food for the elk that in summer range the Gros Ventre Mountains and the southern part of Yellowstone National Park. Even with this provision it is necessary to permit liberal hunting seasons and on occasion to slaughter some of the animals in order to keep the herd in balance with its food supply.

In northern and eastern states the forests of mixed hardwoods and conifers offer ideal summer range, but the big-game herds are limited by the forage available during periods of deep snow. Then the animals concentrate in "yards"—a favorable place is "cedar swamps"—where they winter by keeping feeding trails trampled out in the snow. Too many animals will consume all browse within reach, and starvation ensues. Long continued food shortage may weaken whole herds and even kill the young that cannot reach as high for food as the others. In contrast to snowless ranges, the factor that limits the herd is not the total amount of food but its limited availability in scattered concentration areas. It may be said with a great deal of truth that the maximum deer population that such country can support varies directly with the distribution, number, and size of the cedar swamps.

A quite different picture presents itself in the southeastern mountains, where food limitations are hardly felt but where game populations of all kinds are much below those in less favored areas of other regions. The southern Appalachian region has the food and cover necessary for great game populations, and yet for many years it was relatively the poorest in big-game resources of any natural range in the country. This was due largely to overhunting by a resident population that often is dependent for existence on game and other natural resources. The hunting pressure was so unremitting that game stocks had little opportunity to build up. In recent years better protection, and in some cases restocking has built up good herds of deer in many southern areas. In fact, evidence of local overpopulation is beginning to appear.

These three illustrations regarding deer typify the three main problems of big-game management. The Pennsylvania whitetails have increased in many localities to the point where winter starvation is of regular occurrence and in others is likely to happen almost any year. The Kaibab herd built up to the starvation point and despite drastic reductions in numbers is still limited by very slow recovery in range-carrying capacity. Most of the southern Appalachian deer herds have never attained maximum population in our time because of continual overharvesting.

Where overpopulations already exist, cutting down the numbers of game must be the first step, for the artificial or natural reproduction of food plants is promptly devoured by the hungry animals before any increase in the food supply can be grown. Reducing herds of big game sounds simple, but thus far most attempts to do so systematically have been only partially successful. Eventually, malnutrition or actual starvation will solve the problem, but the wildlife manager feels that this offers a very wasteful and relatively inhumane solution. Driving the animals away from concentration areas has been tried with little success. Deer, in common with other wild things, have definite home territories to which they tend to return. Trapping surpluses and removing the animals to underpopulated areas has been much more successful as a means of stocking new areas than of solving the surplus problem; and the expense of any present method is prohibitive.

Extending hunting privileges in heavily populated areas and opening seasons on the usually protected does have both been tried, and the killing of animals has been found the most logical step toward population decrease. No one plan, however, has been entirely successful for a variety of reasons, among which are lack of hunters to take the desired number of animals, want of skill in those who do hunt, and local public sentiment, which often prevents administrative officials from reducing the herds drastically enough to solve the problem.

All big-game animals that live chiefly in or about forests, as the deer, elk, and woodland caribou, depend for their continuance on a well-planned program of correlating forest management and wildlife management. The program outlined in Chapter Six is applicable especially to deer and elk herds, and if carried out over a long series of years and accompanied by a sensible harvesting of the crop should result in a better adjustment of the big-game populations.

In a number of areas, however, such practices will not overcome the present unbalance between big game and its food supply. In these localities the problem is not one of producing suitable environment but of so managing the wildlife population in any area as to keep it from destroying the environment on which it is dependent. This is a curious and interesting reversal of the process usually thought necessary in wildlife conservation.

It will be seen from this brief survey that management of deer and similar big-game animals involves a minimum of three major concepts: (1) provision of suitable environment; (2) protection of breeding stocks and restocking where necessary; and (3) regulation of the numbers of the animals so as to prevent destruction of environment and consequent decimation of the herds.

Other Browsing and Grazing Species

Deer and elk have been used largely to exemplify the conservation and management problems involved in over-populations of big game. Other big-game mammals subject to management are the caribou, moose, antelope, mountain goat, and bighorn sheep. The caribou is gone as game from this country but still exists in numbers in Canada and Alaska. The principal problem in moose conservation in some areas is apparently that of limiting the kill to something less than the annual increase. In others, notably Newfoundland, areas of overpopulation are present.

Antelopes seemed on the way to extinction in the early 1920's, but long closed seasons, decrease in human populations in their range, and in some cases active predatory-animal control around small remnant herds have restored the antelope populations to the point where a number of states now have open seasons on this fleet-footed species.

Mountain goats seem to be holding their own and perhaps increasing slowly in the limited areas which, often under complete protection, they still occupy in this country. Bighorn sheep, although afforded the protection of closed seasons over most of their range for many years, decreased. While some mountain sheep herds decreased steadily, the knowledge derived from research has helped them in other areas, and there seems to be good reason to believe that populations can be maintained and in many cases increased.

Refuge areas have been set aside specifically for some of these big-game species, and these, together with national parks, primitive areas in national forests, and closed seasons, may preserve the remnants long enough for the factors that limit restoration to be discovered and for means of modifying them to be developed. It is already apparent, however, that the same problem of overpopulation on antelope refuges may some day be present as on certain deer ranges. Deer refuges have been reduced in size or abandoned entirely as the need for them has passed, and it is possible that highly successful restoration of other species may some day require similar action, even though the animals involved are now considered rare or even vanishing.

Quail and Other Small Game

Small resident game species are so restricted in range that they may be successfully managed on relatively small acreages. It is entirely possible for the owner of a single farm to build up a considerable population of quails or rabbits or for the person with a comparatively small woodland to preserve a worthwhile population of grouse or hares.

The bobwhite quail is one of the most widely distributed of small game birds, and from the management standpoint is without doubt the best known of any American game species. In common with all other small animal forms, quails must meet the recurring hazards of climatic extremes (abnormal snowfall, terrific storms, droughts, floods), failure of food supplies (often correlated with climatic conditions), and attacks by diseases and natural enemies. In addition, the bobwhite endures tremendous hunting pressure from which nongame birds are free. While this force may vary widely with locality, the general tendency is for it to become constantly greater. Increased pressure comes not only from increase in the number of hunters but also from heightened effectiveness of firearms and the outstanding development of transportation facilities that has made almost all places readily accessible. Hunters now cover a greater area than formerly, and each has an improved chance of getting his bag limit.

Because of its very restricted year-round range, the bobwhite is an ideal bird for intensive study. Present knowledge indicates that this quail normally spends its entire life within a radius of a mile or less of its birthplace, and many individuals are undoubtedly much more sedentary. This trait alone removes much of the difficulty in studying closely the movements and behavior of individuals and groups.

The limited range of bobwhites has also made more practicable the application of management practices. Obviously it is much more feasible to arrange the proper combination of cover and food on the few acres used by a covey of quails than it is to provide such environmental requirements for creatures that range over thousands of acres. As a matter of fact, good farm management alone, particularly where there is some waste land, will almost automatically improve conditions for the quail and other species that have somewhat similar food and cover requirements.

On the average farm that has a crop rotation including wheat, corn, buckwheat, lespedeza, soy beans, and similar seed producers, there is usually an abundance of quail food. If this is accessible to suitable cover the birds will thrive. On the other hand, clean cultivation, substitution of barbed wire for old rail fences and hedgerows, and grazing every bit of brush or woodland will eliminate the quail even where there is a plentiful food supply.

In certain areas where cover is plentiful, the planting of narrow strips of food-producing crops along the edges of the coverts has greatly increased the quail population. Brushy fence corners and weed- and vine-grown fence rows may not have the prim and neat appearance of a city park, but they furnish a safe retreat for the quail as well as provide it with safe travel-ways for reaching otherwise inaccessible supplies of food.

Soil erosion programs, by planting gullies and galled spots with bushes, trees, and perennial plants, and by strip cropping and proper woodland management, have increased the possibilities of quail survival on thousands of farms. This is another illustration of the close interrelationship of various phases of conservation.

The improvement of environmental conditions suitable for the quail is the most certain to succeed of any method yet devised by the rapidly developing science of wildlife management. Given proper food and shelter, quail populations can thrive despite bad weather and the attacks of natural enemies. The development of better quail environment also is often found to favor the production of greater populations of rabbits as well as of numerous nongame birds and mammals.

Methods of increasing quail populations are well developed and have been applied over wide areas with considerable success. Unfortunately another vital phase of management, that of limiting the kill to the surplus above breeding stocks, has not been so successful. Various approaches have offered some measures of success when tried experimentally, but when applied on a large scale have not been entirely successful. Some of the better-known plans for restricting the kill are:

1. Restrictions on the season during which birds may be hunted, on the number that may be bagged, and on the methods by which they may be taken. These are among the oldest of game-management devices, and when supported by public sentiment they are among the most successful from a practical standpoint. Though such restrictions are now, and probably always will be, violated by unscrupulous hunters, they are usually observed by a large enough percentage of shooters to make them effective. It is certain that without them many more of our birds and mammals would now be with the passenger pigeon and the heath hen.

2. Educational efforts to raise the standards of sportsmanship. These often take the form of trying to get the hunter to be satisfied with a modest bag rather than wanting, like the old meat hunter, "all the law allows (if not more) every time I go into the field." Another phase of sport improvement emphasizes the skill displayed in outwitting the game rather than the kill for the day or season. Both efforts are useful in bringing about a more wholesome attitude toward game and hunting.

3. Adoption of the paid-hunting systems. These have been applied more successfully to large holdings offering such game as deer or turkeys. Overhead expense is often too great to allow the management of quail areas at charges the hunters will pay.

4. The establishment of small refuges, widely scattered, to assure that seed stocks shall be preserved. To be effective for quails, rabbits, or ring-necked pheasants, these need not be large. Theoretically, refuges are sound; but practically, the problem of patrolling them during the hunting season is difficult, and for this and other reasons, many biologists doubt their management value, and many states no longer use small refuges for upland game.

A combination of two or more of these principal means of regulating the kill is usual, and many variations are constantly being tried. This fact gives hope that satisfactory methods of controlling the harvest will ultimately be developed.

Grouse and Squirrels

For two other popular small-game types, grouse and squirrels, woodlots and forested areas, if properly managed, provide favorable environment. The ruffed grouse has been more intensively studied than any other game bird except the bobwhite. It is known definitely that forested areas that contain no grouse can be made suitable for these birds by slashing, cutting fire lanes, and carrying out other operations that open the forest canopy. A large part of the food of the grouse is furnished by understory plants that grow most abundantly in the open or in only moderate shade; and such growth is favored by openings. The ruffed grouse is a bird of the forest edge, and anything that lengthens the edge increases grouse range. Demonstrated both by observation and by experiment, this furnishes one soundly established basic fact that has been most useful in connection with managing land for grouse production. A serious drawback to the proper interpretation of experimental results, as well as to practical management, is the cyclic fluctuation of the grouse population from causes that are as yet far from being understood, despite all the study that has been devoted to the problem.

Squirrels have been given less attention than other small game, and up to very recently it has been customary to take squirrel crops for granted. Beyond the fact that they are woodland mammals that like nuts and seeds, very little of practical value in maintaining or increasing squirrel populations has been known. Within recent years, however, new studies of squirrels have been undertaken, and the findings are much the same as studies for other wildlife species. To be productive, squirrel territory must have plenty of den sites, a variety and quantity of fruits, nuts, and seeds to provide a year-round food supply, and a forest canopy extensive enough to supply safe cover.

For all forest game species, protection of woodlands from excessive grazing and maintenance of openings and forest edges are sound management devices and should be employed wherever practicable. Leaving hollow trees for squirrel dens is also good management.

Intensive management for one or a few species of forest trees, a practice which is appearing in some sections of the country, has caused some concern among wildlife managers. If intensive planting and early harvesting and elimination of competing tree species become widespread, squirrels and other forest game could be seriously affected.

Handling of the harvesting of woodland game is in about the same stage of study and experimentation as is that for quail. There is a growing amount of data that indicate to some extent that the human harvest of small game is self-limiting. As the hunting becomes more difficult, fewer hunters tend to go into the field, and the kill per hunting day decreases. As a result of these findings, there is a tendency to lengthen open seasons and reduce other hunting restrictions.

Game Farming and Restocking

Game farming in America is a practice borrowed from Europe, particularly England. For many years it was regarded by enthusiastic advocates as furnishing the ultimate solution for all game problems. It has required years of experience to demonstrate that useful as the game farm is under some circumstances, there are vast differences between the conditions in this country and in Europe. These have prevented the game farm from fitting as well into the program here as it has on that continent. Game farms are useful as a source of breeding birds to restock depleted areas, but they do not solve the problem of providing a game supply adequate for public shooting.

It is doubtless true that more money has been wasted trying to provide game by artificial methods than by any other single practice yet tried in the United States. Much of this waste could have been avoided by a more intelligent selection of the time and place for releasing artificially reared birds. The fundamental difficulty, however, is more deeply seated. It goes back to the basic difference between the European and American philosophies regarding game. In Europe the game farm is used to supplement natural production on comparatively large holdings over which few people are permitted to shoot. In this country the attempt has been made to use it as an aid to provide shooting for an almost unlimited army of hunters, in some instances in disregard of natural reproduction and in attempts to depend entirely on artificial stocking.

Hence until comparatively recently the game-farm idea has tended to limit attempts to maintain efficient natural production by providing better cover and food conditions. This latter, however, is the surest and most economical method of producing quantities of huntable game that game technicians have yet found. The history of our dealings with game species has been much the same regardless of variations in detail. First, there was great depletion; second, a period of little or no huntable game; third, an expensive and often futile attempt to rear artificially and at public expense stocks of game to release for hunters who pay only a nominal fee for the hunting privilege; and fourth, the development in the last few years of efforts to induce greater natural production by providing as near ideal living conditions as present knowledge will permit. Because of strong pressure from hunters for something to shoot, some administrators are still attempting to carry out artificial restocking, but most game administrators privately admit the total inadequacy of a program that involves only the release of artificially reared birds each one of which may cost more than the seasonal license fee of one hunter.

Other wildlife officials are turning more and more to the idea of producing natural crops of game by protecting brood stock, improving environment to produce maximum crops, and limiting the take to the surplus available. All these are necessary components of this most promising development in game-management practices.

11 / Migratory Birds

For migratory birds the basic requirements are the same as for resident forms. They too must have suitable food and cover available for year-long activities, but these cannot be provided in one place. Many species fly the length of the continent twice a year; others go into South America and return, traversing parts of two continents within twelve months. The breeding and wintering grounds, therefore, lie far apart, and for this reason no local or limited effort to provide for migratory species can be wholly effective. Not only must provision be made for wintering and breeding grounds, but suitable feeding and resting areas between must be available on the migration lanes. This necessitates a broad base for any program intended to benefit these species. The growing recognition of this fact and the results of that recognition have furnished one of the most important advances in wildlife conservation during recent years.

It is a recognized fact that no state, either in this country or in Mexico, no province in Canada, and no one country of these three in its entirety furnishes both breeding and wintering grounds for all the migratory birds that are found within their boundaries at some season of the year. Canada and Alaska, for example, contain the major part of the waterfowl breeding grounds in North America, but the United States and Mexico provide a large part of the equally important wintering areas. Since Mexico and the southern

United States produce few ducks and geese, they must depend for their wintering populations on the nesting grounds far to the north.

The continental aspect of the problem has been recognized in treaties between the United States and Great Britain on the one hand, and the United States and Mexico on the other. The first was ratified on December 8, 1916, and the Mexican treaty on March 15, 1937. There is need for similar treaties with some of the South American and Caribbean countries if all the migratory species that spend some parts of the year in this country are to be assured adequate protection elsewhere.

Different Types of Migrants

In the term "migratory birds," which includes many different types and categories, are embraced those forms that have summer and winter homes more or less widely separated. These can be broadly divided into four groups: (1) song and insectivorous birds; (2) nongame water birds; (3) shorebirds; and (4) game birds.

Song and Insectivorous Birds

Migratory song and insectivorous birds are many and varied. The group contains many of our most beautiful and interesting species. Warblers, vireos, and thrushes are only a few of the many families represented, and this whole group is receiving an increasing degree of international protection. With the exception of the robin, the bobolink, and one or two others sometimes relished as human food, few species of this group have ever been affected by hunting pressure. Many of the man-caused changes on the land do directly affect both the local distribution and the abundance of these birds.

To list only a few of the more conspicuous examples, the cutting of the virgin forests removed habitat for forest birds and consequently greatly reduced their local populations. This action, however, resulted in more favorable habitat for birds adapted to cultivated lands, pastures, or brush areas. The bobolink has spread widely with agricultural development, and the crow has increased appreciably in the Middle West in response to the same change. Drainage of wet lands removes from the local fauna the marsh wrens, blackbirds, and yellowthroats, which prefer habitat of that type, and similarly the replacement of hedges and rail fences with wire has decreased the number of hedgeloving birds.

The response of these birds to changes in environment is inevitable and is another striking example of the close relationship that exists between the various conservation problems of today. This particular group of birds is discussed more fully in a succeeding chapter.

Nongame Water Birds

Nongame water birds in the migratory group include the families of loons, grebes, herons, cormorants, and pelicans. Except locally, few of them have ever been hunted for food or sport. Some have been slaughtered in times past for their plumes, and others are subjected to more or less sporadic persecution because of their supposed destruction of valuable fishes.

Many are large and interesting birds that add a picturesque bit of life to lakes and marshes. All play their part in the food chains that exist on water and land as previously outlined; and all are part of nature's age-old mechanism for building and maintaining productive soils and waters. This latter service alone should assure them of a right to live, and it is sufficient answer to the frequent question, "What good are they?"

The destruction of lakes and marshes has greatly reduced the total environment for the species in this category. It has meant the entire elimination of many from some localities and a great reduction in their numbers elsewhere. Any extensive water-restoration program tends to restore them locally at least, and their quick invasion of restored waters has been an interesting phenomenon. This group also is discussed more in detail in the chapter on nongame species.

Shorebirds

The term "shorebird" includes the snipes, sandpipers, and plovers, together with such smaller and less widely known groups as the stilts, avocets, oystercatchers, turnstones, and others. In contrast to the song, insectivorous, and other nongame species, this group has been greatly reduced by direct hunting pressure. With certain exceptions, to be discussed later, their major breeding grounds are still intact. Many of the species, however, have all but vanished despite this fact and the further significant fact that they were gone before there was any appreciable impairment of their winter homes.

The Eskimo curlew, now nearly if not quite extinct, bred in the barren grounds of northern Canada and wintered in the plains of Argentina, Patagonia, and Chile. The breeding grounds still remain available to the birds as also do a large part of their wintering grounds. Yet the birds are gone, victims of a combination of market hunting and overshooting for sport.

Many of the other shorebirds nest in the barren grounds of Canada and Alaska and winter from the southern United States southward. It was not destruction of their proper environment, but wasteful use that all but destroyed many of these species also. The golden plover, Hudsonian curlew, and pectoral sandpiper are among the numerous forms that belong in this class.

On the other hand, the more southern nesting willets, long-billed curlews, marbled godwits, and upland plovers faced at one and the same time both heavy shooting pressure and the progressive destruction of much of their prairie habitat. Restoration of the grasslands, as discussed in another chapter, would do much for these and similar species, especially if the restoration included both marsh and lake development and revegetation of the uplands.

All these birds have increased in numbers following the closed season established under the migratory-bird treaty with Great Britain, a fact that in itself is another indication of the part overshooting formerly played in their decrease. Putting it another way, if a breeding stock is not saved, an abundance of favorable environment will be useless in producing birds. Realization of this basic truth came too late to save the Eskimo curlew, but it should never be forgotten in any dealing with wildlife problems.

The shorebirds as a group lay but four eggs. Many of them nest so far north that the short seasons give them little chance to lay a second set of eggs and rear a brood if the first set should be destroyed. This limits such birds to a small average production per breeding pair. Most of them travel in flocks from which it is easy to kill great numbers, but there are two notable exceptions—the woodcock and Wilson's snipe. These birds nest farther south over a very large breeding range and travel as individuals rather than in flocks. Their erratic flight furnishes them a measure of protection from all but the more expert wing shots. These two still remain on the game-bird lists, largely because difference in habits offsets to some extent the low reproductive rate shared with other shorebirds. For the other shorebirds, the low rate of reproduction, the flocking habit, the increase in the numbers of hunters, and the improvement in guns produced a combination of conditions that has more or less permanently removed them from the game-bird list.

There is still another factor affecting the golden plover, Hudsonian curlew, upland plover, and many others. These species make their winter home in the grassy plains of South America from Brazil and Peru south to Patagonia. In recent years, large-scale agricultural developments in these countries have invaded their wintering grounds, and the killing of even the rarer species is still almost unrestricted in some parts of their winter homes. For these species little more can be done than has already been attempted in North America, and it is for their protection that treaties similar to those with Canada and Mexico are most urgently needed.

Waterfowl and Other Game Birds

The group of migratory game birds includes ducks, geese, coots, gallinules, and rails, which together have constituted one of America's greatest sources of huntable game. At the time of settlement of this continent there existed in its great marshlands and water areas a population of migratory waterfowl that staggered the imagination of the newcomers. They described its abundance in most extravagant terms, and there is no doubt that the continental population at that time far exceeded that existing today, even though there are no figures available to express it. These migrant game species played an important part in providing food to the earlier settlers. Today they could still be an abundant valuable resource had they not been so wastefully handled in the past.

The alarming decline in their numbers finally focused public attention on their plight. The first result was the negotiation of the Migratory Bird Treaty with Great Britain and adoption subsequently of Federal regulation of the kill. Later (1928), the passage of the Migratory Bird Conservation Act authorized appropriations for the restoration of marshes; the Migratory Bird Hunting Stamp Act (1934) provided a fund for the advancement of a refuge system; and finally the Mexican treaty (1937) supplemented that with Great Britain and brought many new species of birds under Federal protection and helped inaugurate a conservation program in Mexico. These successive acts reflect a growing public understanding of the decrease in the birds and the necessity of some constructive action if this part of the wildlife resource is to be retained.

Factors Adverse to Waterfowl

It will be well at this point to review briefly the causes leading to the desperate conditions for waterfowl that became increasingly apparent from about 1920 to 1935. Three major factors seem all-important: drainage, drought, and long-continued overshooting. In addition, such minor ones as botulism and other diseases, lead poisoning, and predation added their toll and at the same time took much more than their share of the blame for the rapid decrease of the migratory flocks.

Predation will be discussed more fully in another chapter. It is sufficient to point out here that all available evidence indicates that no serious depletion of numbers of waterfowl is caused by predation on adult birds. There is evidence of local destruction of eggs and young by various predators, but all present evidence indicates that such pressure is local rather than extensive and is by no means as important as commonly believed.

Botulism losses have been heavy in many widely scattered localities throughout the West. It is a disease associated with the shallow alkaline lakes and marshes from the Dakotas west to Oregon and California, the serious effect of which has certainly been accentuated by the overcrowding of birds into constantly shrinking water areas. The cause is now known, and where water levels can be controlled the losses can be greatly reduced.

Lead poisoning, caused when spent shot swallowed by the birds is disintegrated and absorbed into the body, takes a constant but unknown toll of waterfowl. Many efforts have been made to reduce this loss by developing some other type of shot as a substitute for that now in use, but no practical results have yet been achieved.

These and similar minor but important factors cause losses of individuals from an already sadly depleted stock; they also help to obscure other causes of loss; and they may do more harm by diverting attention from more important factors than do the actual losses they directly produce.

Drainage

More than 100,000,000 acres of land have been drained in this country. Not all was of primary value to waterfowl, although much of it was used by the birds at some season of the year. The drained areas included many of the best nesting marshes. The breeding grounds in the Prairie Provinces of Canada suffered from the same cause. The loss of these more southern breeding grounds harmfully affected all species of ducks nesting there, though it cut into continental populations of mallards, pintails, baldpates, and other species with extensive breeding range less than it did into those of the canvasbacks, redheads, ruddies, and blue-winged teals, which, nesting farther south, had their most acceptable breeding grounds in the area most directly affected by the drainage program. Similarly many of the best feeding grounds along the migration routes were drained and lost to the birds; and drainage for agriculture, mosquito control, and other purposes has also invaded the important wintering marshes of the United States.

Drought

Dry cycles that extend over long series of years of less than average rainfall over much of the important breeding area in northern United States and southern Canada either greatly dimish waterfowl marshes and lakes still untouched by drainage or destroy them entirely. The combination of these factors shows its effects in several directions. It greatly reduces the amount of favorable environment available to the birds. This alone would inevitably reduce the continental waterfowl population even if all the other adverse factors were absent, since these birds cannot breed or survive without this environment. The constantly shrinking marsh area crowds the remaining waterfowl population into smaller and smaller areas. This great concentration of birds on the remaining water areas has several harmful results: It undoubtedly increases the toll taken by botulism; it makes it easier for hunters to find and take the remaining birds; and, worst of all, by the very density of these concentrations, it leads many to believe that no decrease of the waterfowl population has occurred and that therefore no remedial action is necessary.

Overshooting

Since 1900, the number of hunters has multiplied greatly. At the same time the improvements in firearms and ammunition have increased the effectiveness of the individual gunner, and the development of the automobile with the accompanying building of modern highway systems has greatly extended the territory over which he can hunt in one season. Where formerly game species were largely subjected to hunting pressures only locally, now they must withstand an added pressure from the influx of hunters from a distance. As the migratory birds were forced into more and more restricted areas by drainage and drought, the hunting pressure could be and was applied to them in an increasing degree. Where formerly a few men might have made long trips for the purpose of hunting waterfowl, scores and hundreds have now come to look upon such journeys as a regular part of their hunting schedule. Along with this, the development of such hunting aids as rest days, baiting, and live decoys assured as nearly as was possible the presence of birds on the hunting ground and a chance for a limit bag every shooting day.

Long seasons and comparatively large bag limits, together with the pressure of an increasing number of hunters, combined to accelerate the decline of the waterfowl. In many years the total loss from hunting, both legal and illegal, added to the toll taken by disease, predators, and abnormal climatic conditions, exceeded the crop of young produced by the remaining breeding stock. The best evidence in support of this statement is the unanimous testimony of biologists familiar with the still undisturbed breeding areas in northern Canada and Alaska. All agree (and there is a great deal of supporting testimony from local observers) that these breeding areas are underpopulated. Local observers disagree as to the extent of the decrease. According to locality, they estimate that these areas are now used by only a tenth to a half of the breeding populations of former times.

This condition again emphasizes the necessity of preserving *adequate* breeding stock as the basis of any program of wildlife restoration and management.

Waterfowl Flyways

In order properly to develop a program for the restoration and preservation of migratory waterfowl it is necessary first to review briefly the movements of these birds. Fortunately there exists in the files of the U. S. Fish and Wildlife Service a matchless volume of migration records that have been furnished by a great army of coöperating observers extending back to 1885. There are also the return reports from birds banded since 1910. These furnish an accurate method of studying the movements of individuals. Several hundred thousand returns have been received from all over the Western Hemisphere. Each year more bandings are added to the records by another army of coöperators, the returns from which are constantly adding to the volume of accurate data available.

The information from these two sources reveals that birds move north and south through regular migration routes and that within certain limits they move on a regular schedule. Out of these studies has also come the flyway concept.

A flyway is more than a migration route. In reality it contains the breeding range, the wintering range, and the intervening territory traversed by a great mass of birds twice a year. There are four of these flyways in North America. Each furnishes a year-round home and range for a great variety of ducks and geese many of which stay surprisingly close to their own flyways.

1. The Atlantic Flyway follows the eastern coast of the continent. The birds using this flyway breed over a wide segment of Canada, with two main sources of supply. Black ducks and some Canada geese come from eastern Canada, while brants and greater snow geese nest in the far northern Canadian islands and in Greenland. Still more Canada geese are raised on the west shore of Hudson Bay, and the eastern part of the great Prairie Province nesting area furnishes canvasbacks, redheads, and other ducks. The birds using this flyway winter on the Atlantic coast from New England southward.

2. The Mississippi Flyway is used by birds coming from a breeding territory that extends from the Dakotas and Minnesota north to the Arctic and from Hudson Bay to the interior of Alaska. The principal wintering grounds of this flyway are along the lower Mississippi and on the Gulf coast, though some birds, including most

of the blue-winged teals, go to the West Indies and northern South America.

3. The Central Flyway breeding grounds are in central Alaska and the interior of Canada, and the principal wintering areas are on the Gulf coast of Texas and Mexico.

4. The Pacific Flyway receives its cackling geese and some of its mallards, pintails, and baldpates from the Alaskan coast. It has large and productive breeding areas in Oregon, Washington, and Idaho and also in British Columbia, Alberta, and the Territories to the north in Canada. The wintering grounds are principally in western Mexico and such areas as are available in California.

The accompanying maps (Figs. 8-11) indicate clearly the scope of the flyways. It is evident that breeding birds belonging to two or more flyways may be found in the same area. In fact, there is definite evidence from returns from banded birds that the same marsh can and does send birds into different flyways (see Fig. 12, Malheur Refuge). There is also a growing mass of evidence to indicate that after a bird has once chosen its summer and winter homes and a travel route between them it strongly tends to stay with that choice.

The cackling goose, with a limited breeding range on the Bering Sea coast of Alaska, indicates the definite tendency to follow the same annual routine. Its travels have been well mapped by the recovery of birds banded on the breeding grounds. These show that cackling geese travel down the coast until they reach the mouth of the Columbia River, when they turn inland and cross the Cascades to Tule Lake, in California. From there they later move to the Sacramento Valley, where they remain until the northward flight is made over the same route.

The geese furnish a vivid illustration of the importance of protecting a breeding stock while the birds are in winter quarters. Except the Canada goose, which nests in this country and southern Canada as well as farther north, every North American goose breeds in the far north beyond any destructive influence that has yet menaced the breeding grounds. In other words, since their nesting

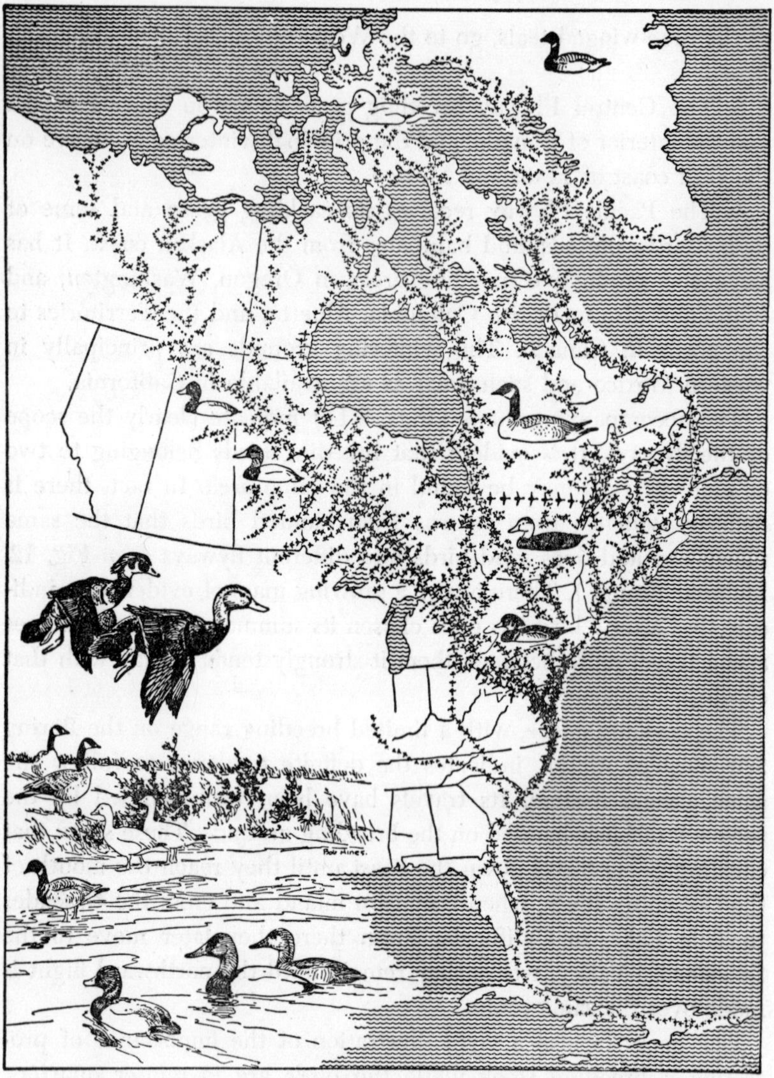

Fig. 8 / The Atlantic Flyway, from a drawing by Robert Hines.
(Photograph No. B-65885, U.S. Fish and Wildlife Service)

Fig. 9 / The Mississippi Flyway, from a drawing by Robert Hines.
(Photograph No. B-65886, U.S. Fish and Wildlife service)

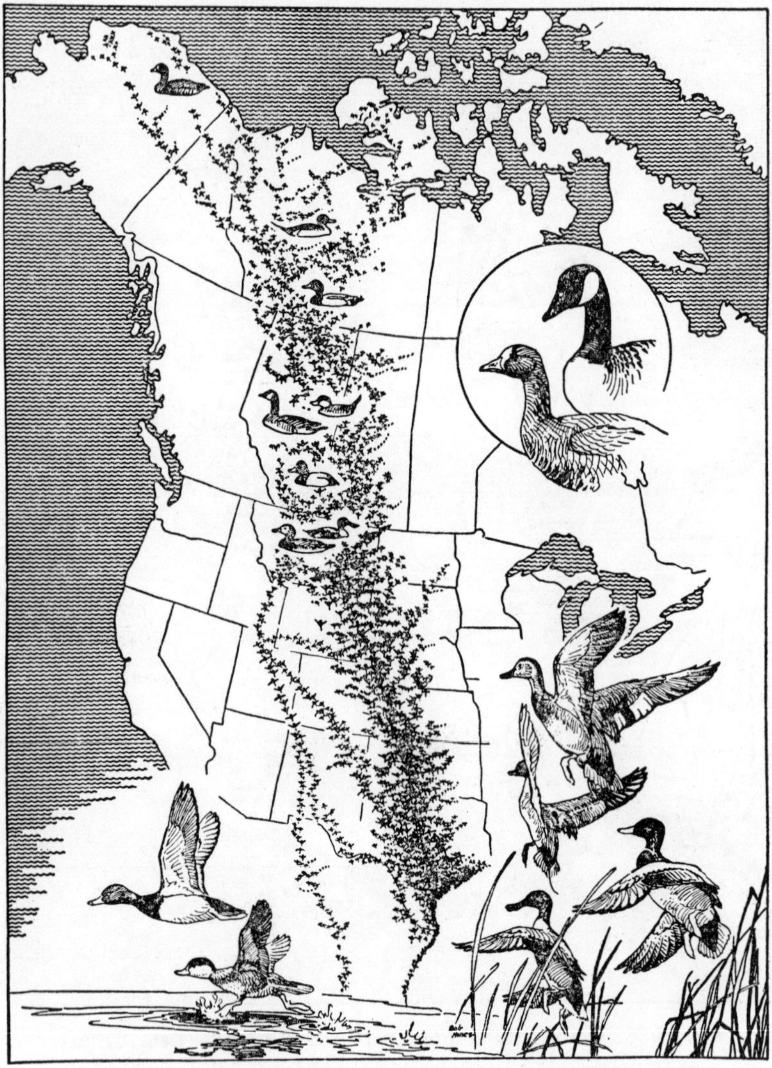

Fig. 10 / **The Central Flyway, from a drawing by Robert Hines.** (Photograph No. B-65887, U.S. Fish and Wildlife Service)

Fig. 11 / The Pacific Flyway, from a drawing by Robert Hines.
(Photograph No. B-65888, U.S. Fish and Wildlife Service)

Fig. 12 / Distribution, by states, of recovery records of ducks banded at Malheur Migratory Bird Refuge in Oregon, chiefly mallards, pintails, baldpates, gadwalls, and green-winged teals. The records become scattering in flyways other than the Pacific, where the banding station is located.

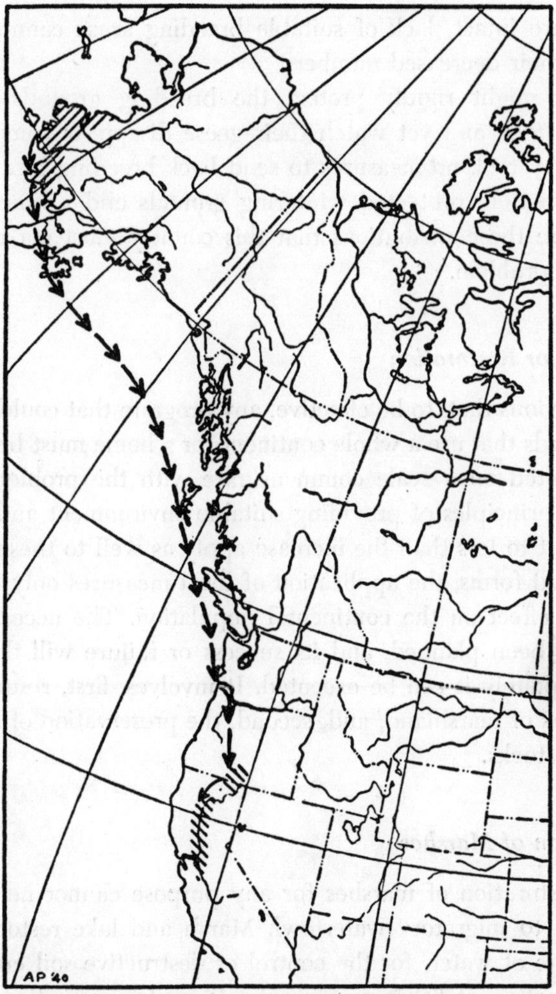

Fig. 13 / Distribution and migration of the diminutive cackling goose, which breeds chiefly along the coast of western Alaska and in winter concentrates at the Tule Lake Wildlife Refuge on the Oregon-California line and in the Sacramento Valley of California. The migration route has been determined by recovery records of birds banded on their nesting grounds.

grounds are intact, lack of suitable breeding areas cannot be the cause of their decreased numbers.

Canada might rigidly protect the breeding grounds and the breeding stock and yet watch their geese disappear completely if this country took no measures to send back breeding birds. Therefore, adequately protected wintering grounds and a limitation on the kill are the contributions that this country must make to help solve this problem.

Program for Restoration

It is obvious that, to be effective, any program that could possibly benefit birds that use a whole continent for a home must be planned and executed on a scale commensurate with the problem. While the basic principles of providing suitable environment and limiting the harvest to less than the increase apply as well to these birds as to localized forms, the application of local measures only can have but little effect on the continental population. The necessary program has been planned, and its success or failure will depend on how completely it can be executed. It involves, first, restoration of large areas of marshland; and, second, the preservation of adequate breeding stocks.

Restoration of Marshes

The restoration of marshes for any purpose cannot help but be beneficial to migratory waterfowl. Marsh and lake restoration for the storage of water, for the control of destructive soil erosion, for the production of fishes or fur animals, or for recreation, in each case contributes in some measure to help the birds. Conversely, definite restoration projects undertaken primarily for migratory waterfowl are all contributory to one or more of these other programs.

The Federal restoration program, based on the Migratory Bird Conservation and Hunting Stamp Acts, has been based on the knowledge of the movements, concentration points, and needs of the birds as learned from the long-time studies referred to in preceding paragraphs. It contemplates the ultimate restoration and development as federal refuges of a minimum of 7,500,000 acres and 5,000,000 acres of state areas primarily for waterfowl. These areas must be distributed among the breeding, resting, and wintering areas if the birds are to be properly cared for while in this country. In addition to this minimum project there are thousands of smaller lakes and marshes, the restoration of which would contribute to the success of the whole program. These furnish a fruitful field for local restoration activities and would benefit both upland and migratory species. The establishment of refuges is more fully discussed in another chapter, but it is desirable here to indicate the essential function of refuges in the solution of the migratory-waterfowl problem.

Preserving Breeding Stock

Because of the depletion of the waterfowl stocks it is necessary now, and probably will be for some time to come, to endeavor to return annually as many or more birds to the breeding grounds as returned the previous year. Two tools are available (with present knowledge) to accomplish this vitally important task.

A refuge system is one of these tools. In addition to restoring or preserving absolutely necessary acreages for breeding, feeding, and wintering, it also serves the equally important function of furnishing sanctuary for the birds during hunting seasons. As the system grows, the insurance that it furnishes the birds will increase in importance.

The other tool is the oldest game-management device used in this country and one that will in some degree always be necessary. That device is the limitation of the annual harvest by prescribing hunting seasons, fixing bag limits, and restricting the time and manner in which the birds may be taken. With due regard to losses from all other causes, these restrictions must be drastic enough to limit the legal harvest to a figure somewhat less than the crop produced that season.

It is easy to outline the basic principles but an exceedingly difficult and intricate task to estimate, even crudely, the total number of birds on the continent and the proportion of that number that may be safely harvested each year. It involves efforts to learn the numbers of birds on winter concentration areas, appraisal of conditions along the migration routes, the success of the birds in producing a crop of young, and year by year comparisons of conditions of the birds on the same area by the same observers in so far as that is possible.

The development of a nation-wide refuge system will gradually build up a better background of check areas with qualified personnel to make seasonal comparisons at frequent intervals. Flyway biologists, each assigned to a definite area, are rapidly building a more comprehensive background of personal observation, which should make the forecasts more accurate as time goes on. Several thousand volunteer observers check and report on various phases of the movements and numbers of birds in their own localities. These reports, together with those from state and Canadian game officials and the reports of U. S. Fish and Wildlife Service personnel, furnish the basic information on which these annual regulations are made.

The amount of information received on the condition of the waterfowl populations has been greatly increased since the four flyway councils were formed. All states participate to some extent in gathering kill statistics, production (in breeding areas), and migration information. The states also have participated in the wetlands surveys designed to classify the remaining wetland for their waterfowl value and to pinpoint the areas in which federal or state acquisition is most important. Most states now have biologists assigned specifically to waterfowl work, and there is a wide appreciation of waterfowl needs. The flyway councils serve a most useful purpose in coordinating information, but have one drawback in the tendency, which sometimes appears, to become pressure groups for changes in regulations when the information available fails to justify such changes.

The policy of limiting the harvest has demonstrated its soundness, but it has not yet reached the goal of restoring adequate breeding stocks both to the continental breeding grounds now available and to those that can and should be restored and of caring for the birds throughout the year. If the marsh-restoration program can be carried forward to completion and the bird population rebuilt to occupy all available marshes, the granting of a greater total annual harvest with safety to the breeding stocks can be anticipated. The good old days of hundreds of birds per day and thousands per season for a single hunting party, however, can never return. The producing plant will not provide so great a crop, but with care it will be possible to allow a reasonable harvest.

On the other hand, if for any reason such a program, or a better one if possible, cannot be completed, there is little hope for the future of the migratory-waterfowl resource. The birds will be seen in decreasing numbers until only a few will be left to use the refuge areas. In that case, the refuge system, designed to safeguard and help increase the supply of birds, may degenerate into a series of outdoor zoos for waterfowl, harboring only a remnant of the once magnificent squadrons.

12 / Fur Animals

During the early settlement of this country fur animals provided one of the great sources of income for the nation, and yet no class of wildlife was more ruthlessly exploited. Pursuit of the fur wealth was the incentive for the exploration of much of the country. Ever since the time of Daniel Boone, a great deal of romance has been woven around the exploits of the wandering trappers and hunters. The average fur trapper of the early days, however, far from being a romantic and noble gentleman, was, in fact, so wild and hard an individual that when occasion demanded he could outdo the Indian in ruthlessness and craftiness. Perhaps, however, it was only through his savagery that he could win through and come back with the store of rich furs he was seeking. His behavior, however, is not set up as a model for the youth of this day.

A Resource Early Exploited

The country that for centuries had furnished fur to the Indians was in a few years practically stripped of it by the greedy fur traders, who made the market for the white trappers and for the Indians as well. According to tradition, whenever it seemed safe to do so, they robbed trappers of both races impartially and allowed very little of the value of the furs to reach those who endured the hardships of the trail and trap line in the wilderness.

As early as 1825 trappers were pushing far back into the wilds of the Pacific Northwest, the last great unexploited fur area within the present boundaries of the United States. Looking for beavers, they stripped the streams of them as rapidly as found, in the final interest of the Hudson's Bay Company, the Astors, and other American traders. Naturally, the decline of the fur resource was rapid. There are no records to indicate its probable value at the time of its greatest abundance, but even if statistics were available, the prices in those times could not be fairly compared with those of today.

At a somewhat later period, when the American fur trade had reached its peak, raw furs collected in the United States had a value of approximately $100,000,000 annually. Their present valuation has shrunk to less than half of that amount in the average year. Comparisons of fur values are all the more difficult because of the widely fluctuating prices paid for pelts of the various species. These vary according to fashion and season; one year beaver fur may be in greatest demand, and a few years later mink, fox, or skunk may be fashionable. The changing dictates of fashion greatly influence the demands and price fluctuations.

Restoration Possible

With the growing interest in the management of fur animals it may be assumed that there is still a chance to restore them to something of their productive value of many years ago. The beaver furnishes an example. Most sought of the early fur animals, this species was practically gone in the United States by 1917 and it remained at a low ebb until about 1927, when a growing realization of its value brought about re-introductions into areas long depleted. Today the beaver population of the United States is certainly many times greater than at the minimum level.

The restoration and development of the fur resources are fraught with many difficulties. We know less about the life histories and needs of these animals and of proper methods of regulating the take than about almost any other kind of wildlife of economic importance. The problem is also complicated by the fact that most fur animals are widely regarded as vermin—to be killed on sight as enemies of game and of poultry and other domestic animals. The administration of this natural resource and legislation regarding it have brought little or no income to most state treasuries; hence state game officials have been able to do little for this kind of wildlife. Recently it has received more attention, but the research needed as a basis for sound management is still woefully inadequate for many species.

A national program for the conservation of fur animals requires much more scientific knowledge than we now have of their life histories, their food and shelter requirements, and their breeding habits. In addition, more knowledge is necessary as to their prime-fur periods and to what extent the fur crop can be harvested from a given area and still leave ample breeding stock. Despite the lack of detailed information, it is known that in general the principles underlying the conservation, restoration, and stabilization of the populations of fur animals are the same as for other wildlife: if these animals are to live, thrive, and increase enough to produce an annual harvest, the environment must be right; there must be provided the right kind of cover or living conditions; and the proper quantity of food must be available for year-around consumption.

From the management standpoint, fur animals can be broadly divided into two groups: (1) Those that must have wilderness if they are to be restored and harvested at all; and (2) those that can live about cultivated lands. Some species can live in both environments, but some can never be permitted to become abundant in agricultural areas. Each group presents different management problems, and for their basic needs different provisions will be necessary.

Wild-Land Species

In considering the possibilities of fur production on wild land, it becomes obvious that the animals involved are again of two types:

(1) Those that inhabit forest and other uplands; and (2) those that require water or marsh areas. Any one of the species found on farms may be produced to a considerable extent on wild lands, but there are several of the wild-land species that cannot be produced in agricultural sections. The great majority of fur animals are predators, the outstanding exceptions being the beaver and the muskrat. Typical forest species are the beaver, marten, fisher, and wolverine, and these exceedingly valuable forms can never be produced in settled areas. The beaver in early years probably was most valuable of all. If the stock had not been forced so low, it could now be producing an annual income large enough to be distributed among people who greatly need it, that is, the persons living in communities bordering on forest lands who add trapping to their varied list of part-time employments.

Coyotes, wolves, foxes, bobcats, mountain lions, and bears, most of which are of widely fluctuating value for their fur, may also be considered here as elements of the fur-conservation problem. Of these, the coyote, fox and bobcat are occasionally of considerable value when fashion swings toward these types of fur. In other years, the price for them is so low that it does not pay trappers to operate the extensive trap lines necessary to catch them in numbers. Bearskins for periods of years had very little or no market value except as trophies, and often brought so little that they did not pay for the labor of skinning and curing. Wolves, particularly those occurring in the southern part of the United States, are in somewhat the same position. They are seldom valuable enough to justify the effort to collect and care for their pelts.

Water and marshland species are the muskrat, mink, and otter, all of which exist sparingly also in farming areas.

Forest and Upland Fur Animals

A serious obstacle to any program of restoration of fur animals, even the more valuable ones, is that the forests and other public wild lands have for many years been regarded as open country for anyone desiring to capture them. Trapping being practically unregulated, the number of trappers has been so great that the forest and upland fur resources have been depleted. Competition for pelts has often resulted in the taking of furs before they were prime. Half-grown beavers that had not yet produced a valuable coat of fur have been caught and sent to the market—the result of one trapper desperately trying to beat another in getting the skins. If trapping had been delayed for a month or six weeks, the skins would have been prime and worth many times the price received.

Another obstacle to be overcome before any intelligent program for the conservation of upland fur animals can be put into effect is the indifference of wildlife administrators. Many of these have not shown much interest in the fur resource because it promises no immediate income for their departments. All state wildlife organizations are run entirely on license fees collected for hunting and fishing privileges, and even where the fees from trapping licenses are available, they are too small to bring in enough funds to be useful in building up the stocks of fur animals. Wildlife administrators are always under pressure from those who hunt and fish to spend on fish and game restoration many times the amount of the available funds. Therefore, the difficulty of developing constructive fur-animal conservation programs has been great.

A third major obstacle may be found in old laws, which stand in the way of rational management of fur animals. Any attempt, however, to change them is fiercely resented both by shortsighted fur dealers and by some trappers, many of whom feel that any interference with their right to trap is not only an invasion of their personal liberty but a threat to their livelihood.

The only practical solution yet suggested for some of the difficulties besetting the conservation of forest and upland fur species is a system of government control of trapping on public lands, which embrace most of the remaining wilderness of the country. In some regions large tracts are still owned by private timber and livestock companies, but these holdings also might be put under an intelligent management for fur animals to the ultimate great advantage of the people who own the land, to their communities, and to the nation.

The first requisite is to limit the take on understocked areas to a point definitely below the annual production, in order that the stocks may build up to something near the carrying capacity of the environment. Some of the Provincial governments in Canada are using a system of leasing public land or issuing permits for trapping on definite areas, with the understanding that so long as the trapper intelligently manages his area and tries to build up the fur stocks his permit will be renewed annually. This makes it to the interest of the trapper himself to see that the stocks are not seriously depleted, for not only will he have available the crop for the year but he is assured that in the next year he will be able to harvest the crop produced under intelligent management. So far as it goes, the plan is good, and has been slowly spreading.

As already mentioned, there is today, in many states, a definite effort to restock and rebuild fur-animal populations. Beavers have been captured alive in cultivated districts where they have become nuisances of the first order and moved to headwaters of streams having plenty of natural food. This circumvents their habit of cutting down fruit trees and their dam-building proclivities, often the cause of flooded roads, meadows, and crop lands. Such transfers relieve the situation by placing these animals where they are not only harmless but actually beneficial. Their dams regulate the flow in small streams and keep them running through the summer in places where, without dams, the water would run off earlier in spring and the streams go dry. The beaver dams also help control soil erosion and in sufficiently elevated, and, therefore, cool, areas create admirable trout-rearing ponds. This restocking program has been so successful that there are open trapping seasons in many states. In fact, beavers have become numerous enough to become troublesome in a number of states.

In relation to trout, the restoration of the beaver at lower altitudes in the eastern states has in some cases spread out the more sluggish streams through their dam building to a point where the water became too warm for these fishes. Considerable complaint has been made in Michigan and in Pennsylvania of the effect of beaver dams on trout streams.

Water and Marshland Species

Thus far little has been done in the way of management and development for the marten, otter, fisher, and wolverine, the remaining most valuable wild-land species. All these animals are predatory, but the marten and fisher feed largely on small rodents and other rapidly reproducing forms to which they can do little harm, and only occasionally in the wild areas frequented do they have opportunity to prey upon any more valuable animals. Otters are water lovers that could be produced in much greater numbers than at present. They could also be encouraged in farming communities and on the larger streams, in many cases without undue damage to human interests. Although they eat fish, there is no evidence that a moderate population of these valuable fur animals would unduly deplete the fish supply as many things other than fish enter into their diet.

The first necessity for all of these species in depleted areas is a closed season of several years' duration, long enough to give the scanty remaining stock a chance to build up into one that will repay management. All except the otter are near the vanishing point. Only a few states have remnants of these species and many states have declared a closed season on one or more species for varying periods. The otter has shown remarkable capacity for survival under difficult conditions but still is in reduced numbers in many areas.

All these species can be produced on wild land without undue interference with any other values. All are predatory to some extent on fishes, on small mammals or small birds, and therefore suffer at the hands of persons having the "vermin" complex. This has already been mentioned and will be dealt with in greater detail in the discussion of fur animals in relation to agricultural land. The mink can well be classed with the wild-land group, although it is wider ranging and capable of surviving in agricultural surroundings. It is still one of the important fur producers, although the annual production is much reduced.

In the marshlands the muskrat leads in fur-producing value—in fact it brings the greatest financial return of any single fur-bearer in the United States. It is prolific, widely distributed, and still abundant in the coastal marshland as well as in the interior. Muskrats respond quickly to favorable conditions. On some of the most profitable marshlands in the United States, notably those in Delaware, on the Eastern Shore of Maryland, and in Louisiana, muskrats are handled on the annual-crop basis and are carefully harvested at the proper season. The income from some of these lands is considerable, and a good muskrat marsh often yields a greater net return per acre than nearby farmlands. Exaggerated ideas of the profits of this business, however, have caused the loss of much money by people who have tried to raise muskrats in pens. The return from muskrats lies in the number that can be produced rather than in the value of the individual; hence they can be produced at a profit only where quantities of their natural foods are available.

Management has progressed further with respect to muskrats than for other fur species. Production in some of the muskrat marshes is most encouraging, but careful study directed toward the improvement of management and increased and more stabilized production undoubtedly would yield a large return.

Farmland Species

Although all fur animals classed as farmland species can be produced on wild land, most of the present supply live in agricultural areas. Most of the muskrat, skunk, raccoon, opossum, and weasel pelts are taken by farm families or by those who have seasonal occupations from which they are free a few weeks or months in the winter. The catch in most areas no longer warrants full-time trapping, but the total production of farm furs is considerable and can be greatly increased whenever the price of the pelts is sufficient to justify the effort necessary to catch the animals and care for the skins.

Muskrats have already been discussed as denizens of wild land, and they can be produced in agricultural areas without serious interference with farming. Every sluggish stream east of the 100th meridian produces a crop of muskrats, but it might be possible to increase the numbers in many areas. It is only in some of the great coastal marshes and in a few of the larger fresh-water marshes on which the owners practice controlled harvesting that the muskrat is still abundant. On other areas, lack of management and uncontrolled competition in trapping result in the harvesting of much fur that is practically worthless and often keeps the breeding population low.

Plans for restoring some of the farm fur animals must be advanced with caution and worked out with due regard for other uses of the land. In the great wheat areas of the Plains states, for example, an increased crop of skunks might very well be produced without undesirable results, as there are few or no chickens for them to bother on most farms. On the other hand, attempts to build up the skunk population in the intensively cultivated sections of Iowa or Illinois, where every farm produces poultry, would be bitterly opposed. One possible method of approach in such communities would be to encourage the idea not of producing more skunks, but of harvesting them in winter, when the fur is prime, rather than killing them at every opportunity, although even this form of management would probably make slow headway. Weasels are in about the same situation, and in the average year the value of their fur is even lower than that of the skunk.

One other obstacle to the restoration of these two species remains to be mentioned, that is, the aversion many people have to handling and skinning them. This distaste, together with the low price the furs bring, discourages any real attempt at management of these two animals in prosperous sections of the country. The most feasible method at present, as with other farm fur animals, would be to encourage taking them at the time they will bring the greatest cash return.

Raccoons and opossums to a lesser extent are hunted with dogs in some sections and are there considered sporting animals. Their fur value, however, is low, and because of their omnivorous habits it is probable that any considerable increase in their population in agricultural sections would bring prompt objections.

Minks and otters might well be increased if the take could be controlled. Their fur is worth so much more than that of any of the other small fur-bearing animals found in agricultural sections that the sight of one is almost an instant signal for every farmer or farm boy in the community to go into action with gun, trap or pitchfork in an endeavor to get that valuable pelt before someone else does. Many people do not realize the necessity of taking fur only in the prime season until after they have killed and skinned an animal, cured the pelt, and sent it to a fur house or sold it to a fur dealer, only to be disappointed at the low price received. Even then some are entirely ignorant of the fact that the fur might have been worth many times what they received if it had been taken at the proper season. There is some hope that, by popular education and development of definite management programs, based on greater knowledge of the value and the needs of fur animals, populations of minks and otters may be increased. Among the fur species that can be produced in an agricultural community with the least complications, muskrats offer the greatest possibilities.

There is as yet little that is definitely known about a farm fur-animal program. It is clear that inflexible laws, improper management practices, and lack of interest in producing a greater number are the principal difficulties in the way of restoring these species.

Status of Fur Animals

With proper management of fur animals, there is in the wild lands of the United States, both upland and marsh, a potential source of revenue that can be increased over that now received, without interference with any other purpose for which the lands may be used. The national forests, especially those that lie in great belts along the upper slopes of the western ranges, might well be producing many times the fur value that is now being realized, and this without any appreciable encroachment upon forestry, grazing, or other uses of these reservations.

In view of the scanty knowledge of the needs of some of the valuable fur animals, including the marten, fisher, otter, mink, and wolverine, proper protection and the regulation of the take are the only things that can at present be recommended as steps toward their management. Their numbers can be much greater than at present without clashing with other interests.

In contrast to most of the other wild-land fur animals, bears, little exploited for fur, have increased appreciably in the past few years, and there are now numbers of them in many of the forested areas both in the western states and in the eastern part of the country. In many states they are regarded as game, while in others they are still classed as predators or fur animals and no protection is given them. Whenever they have a chance, they increase, and they are now fairly common in many states in which they were at a low ebb in the early part of this century.

The great timber wolves of the northern states are almost gone. Their predatory propensities spelled their doom on livestock ranges many years ago. There are still a few small bands in wildernesses, and from the biological standpoint it certainly would be regretted if finally they were to be completely exterminated. On the other hand, in agricultural and livestock-producing sections they present very serious problems and it is probable that any stock of these magnificent predators that may be retained in the future must be on preserves dedicated to them.

Coyotes and bobcats, often classed as fur animals and of considerable value to the fur trade in some years, are considered predators throughout their range and are afforded no protection. There seems to be little danger of exterminating either, particularly the coyote, which is highly adaptable and abundantly able to care for itself.

The coyote has steadily extended its range until it presents a unique problem. Originally confined to the Plains, it has invaded agricultural areas east of its former normal range and has gone into every mountain range in the West—territory that was formerly coyote-free. It has also penetrated the Yukon country and eastern Alaska. No protection is afforded it anywhere, and despite the fact that the animal is always fair game it not only succeeds in holding its own but in some areas has actually increased in numbers.

In fur value the bobcat, or wildcat, is in about the same class as the coyote, and although it has not increased and spread to the same extent, it retains much of its original wide distribution.

The fox is still widely distributed through most of its former range and like the coyote is in no danger of extermination. It is protected in a number of eastern states, not as a fur animal but as game that is hunted with horses and hounds. In the United States there is little protection afforded it because of pelt value, although in parts of Canada and Alaska it is recognized as one of the more valuable fur-producers.

It will be seen from this somewhat brief sketch of the present abundance of fur animals that in any program for their restoration several kinds and degrees of problems will be involved. The chief difficulties that should be overcome are absence of flexible laws to permit intelligent management and lack of sound management technique. The group of fur animals that produce the most valuable pelts are so near extermination that there should be no delay in giving them protection for a period of years. In a second class are beavers and bears, which are definitely on the increase, thanks to management methods that have been successfully developed. A third category includes the coyote, an animal that is still abundant and in no danger of extermination, although it is afforded no protection and is generally considered "vermin" to be killed at any time.

From the management viewpoint there are real possibilities among the fur animals, and first efforts should be directed toward restoring those that furnish the most valuable fur. The marten, otter, fisher, wolverine, and mink on forested lands and the muskrat in marsh areas are in this class.

A hopeful sign is the increasing interest in fur-animal research. A number of universities are sponsoring studies of animal problems and some of the states likewise are approaching this subject from the management and administration standpoint. It is certain, therefore, that in a few years a greater body of knowledge will be available than now and that at present fur-animal restoration is only beginning to emerge from the field of wishful thinking to become a definite effort to accomplish practical results.

13 / Nongame Birds and Mammals

Among the many forms of wild birds and mammals are some that man does not classify as game, fur animals, or major predators, and yet that are too abundant and widespread to be treated as rare or vanishing species (see Chapter Fourteen). A single chapter is here devoted to them, because all fill a place in the natural processes already discussed and because some of their relationships to human needs and plans have been the cause of much controversy.

These chiefly nongame forms can be considered to fall largely into two categories, according to the real or imaginary effect they may have for good or ill on human interests. This division is somewhat artificial, as few, if any, forms of wildlife can be considered as having either entirely beneficial or entirely harmful economic relations. They can be considered valuable or objectionable only as their habits of life affect man's interests. On any other basis, all living forms, even weeds and the worst animal pests, are useful elements in the natural community and in the natural processes of building and maintaining fertile soils, conserving water, and providing a supply of plant and animal food for all life.

Valuable species may be defined as those that man has come to feel are of direct use to him or that, in the absence of direct harm, he may enjoy having about because of their beauty of form or color, pleasing song, or interesting ways. Naturally there will be little agreement among groups of varied interests as to the class in which a specific form should be placed. Bird enthusiasts would class all feathered animals as valuable, while at the other extreme there are individuals who would class as either useless or "vermin" all forms that are not locally taken for food, sport, fur, or some other purpose useful to man. In this discussion the species treated as valuable are divided into two groups—those having some economic use and those that have chiefly an esthetic appeal.

Economically Valuable Wildlife

Omitting the game and fur species already discussed, the forms generally considered of greatest economic value are those that prey on the insects that are harmful to man's interests. This group includes the bats and a few other mammals and the insect-eating birds—in short a varied assortment of species that are predators on the insect world. Detailed studies have been made of the food habits of the birds falling in this class and of many other vertebrates, and a great mass of information has been developed.

There is no question that many kinds of birds, individually and collectively, do destroy enormous numbers of insects. Neither is there any doubt that such destruction exerts a pressure on insects that tends to reduce the damage they cause. As will be pointed out in the chapter on predation, however, there is as yet little evidence of any practical economic effect of such pressure. In other words, no method has yet been devised to bring about an actual increase in crop production, or, if not an increase, a decrease in the expense or effort required to produce a crop, by relying solely upon the agency of birds as insect destroyers.

Ornithologists generally believe that such pressures are great aids to agriculture and forestry, basing that belief on the enormous numbers of insects destroyed by individual birds or by the total bird population of a given territory. Many believe that the repressive effects of birds are of greater value during periods of insect scarcity and of less value when there are great insect outbreaks. Entomologists, on the other hand, emphasizing perhaps unduly the enormous reproductive potential of insects, feel that climatic conditions, diseases, and parasites are much more important agencies than are birds in holding insect populations in check.

Regardless of which may prove to be the correct view of this complex and intricate relationship, it is certain that the insectivorous proclivities of birds are one factor in controlling insects—probably most effective in slowing up an increase in numbers when insects have been reduced numerically by other means—and that because of the pressure thus exerted, the birds should be left to pursue that avocation unless they otherwise adversely affect man's interests.

Bats, although less widely appreciated, act in the same capacity, as do also toads and certain species of mice and squirrels. Skunks, foxes, and coyotes, to mention only a few represent other mammals that feed on insects to some extent. None of these forms is abundant enough in most localities, however, to equal the repressive effect of insectivorous birds, and therefore their combined effect is even less visible than that of birds.

Species of Esthetic Value

Birds are popularly regarded as having the greatest esthetic value of any class of wildlife, although there is no real reason why the same kind of pleasure should not be derived from mammals, insects, toads, or any other living forms. In fact, to a much smaller but just as appreciative audience, many living forms other than birds do give real pleasure. The majestic carriage of an elk, the grace of a deer, the speed of an antelope, the leap of a salmon, the swift swoop of a hawk, the delicate tracery of a spider's web, the sheen of a butterfly's wing, the audacity of a squirrel, and countless other characteristics appeal to the esthetic in humanity.

Perhaps the basic reason that birds furnish esthetic enjoyment to more people than do other classes of wildlife is found in their proximity and availability. Birds are everywhere that human beings may be, whether in the wilderness or in a city back yard or park. Many are brightly colored and many also have beautiful songs. Therefore the opportunity to enjoy birds comes to more people than do similar opportunities to watch other forms of wildlife, particularly those found in more remote places. Although some minimize the importance of the esthetic, there has been a growing popular appreciation of its value to those who, under modern conditions, have limited opportunities to enjoy the presence of wildlife.

Curiously enough, the destruction of "plumage" birds to obtain decorations for ladies' hats (paradoxically an esthetic demand) provided the stimulus that developed into a crusade to preserve the bird victims. Later it expanded into a general educational program for all bird protection based on economic and esthetic grounds. Egrets, herons, terns, gulls, grebes, and many other plumage birds had for years been subjected to a relentless persecution by professional plume hunters, who killed thousands for a few feathers. In the case of egrets, the most valuable feathers were carried by the birds during the nesting season only, and when the adults were killed for their plumes, the uncared-for young in the nests died of starvation. Publicizing this inhumanity greatly aided the crusade against the trade in plumage, not only of egrets but of other birds as well. That public sentiment and legislation in time combined to end it has been well portrayed by T. Gilbert Pearson in his book, *Adventures in Bird Protection.** As a result of this effective public crusade, the remnants of great rookeries of the persecuted birds were preserved. These birds—on the verge of extinction at the height of the plumage trade—have increased and are again occupying their old nesting grounds, where they are picturesque elements in the life of many marshes from which they had long been absent.

The colonies of terns, which were practically extirpated along the Atlantic coast, have greatly increased, and these graceful sea sprites are again to be seen regularly in many of their old haunts. The protection of the gulls has been almost too successful, as they

* Pearson, Thomas Gilbert. *Adventures in Bird Protection: An Autobiography by Thomas Gilbert Pearson: With an Introduction by Frank M. Chapman.* 459 pp., illus. New York, London, 1937.

are now showing a strong tendency to drive out other island-nesting species. The grebes and herons also have increased and spread somewhat, although the general tendency of gunners to use any large bird for a target has retarded the increase of those that are wide ranging.

The return of the species formerly slaughtered for their plumage was the first large-scale restoration of birds in this country, and its effect on conservation thought has been great. It has demonstrated beyond question that legal protection by closed seasons, backed by public sentiment, can effectively restore species whose habitat has not also been destroyed. Now the destruction of habitat by drainage and for agricultural and urban development is again threatening some of the forms that provided the impetus for the original crusade for protection.

The same conservation forces and sentiments that saved the plumage birds have also helped many others. Small birds, both song and insectivorous, with a combination of confiding ways, interesting habits, brilliant plumage, and beautiful songs, are attractive subjects for similar educational efforts. All have profited much from such programs, although at times some followers of popular ornithology have become so fanatical in devotion to their cause that their insistence on extreme measures may have hampered more practical efforts to help their favorites.

Many activities in general wildlife programs have contributed to the welfare of small birds. Wildlife refuges, no matter what their main objective, help many small forms by preserving suitable homes and adequate food supplies, and many soil-conservation projects provide favorable wildlife environment where none existed before. The planting of hedges, gullies, and contour slopes in soil-erosion control adds to the areas available to the birds that require such conditions. Marsh and lake restoration programs are already making substantial progress and are contributing directly to the welfare of water-loving birds, among them many formerly slaughtered for their plumage. Reforestation programs, in covering barren lands with vegetation, also contribute directly and effectively to the welfare of many forms. In addition to the incidental benefits accruing to many species, direct efforts have been made to increase and protect small birds. People have been encouraged to plant trees and shrubs about their homes not only for the ornamental effects but also to provide food and homes for birds. With a little thought it is usually easy to obtain both values from one planting.

The interest in providing bird homes, bird baths, and feeding stations, promoting bird-house-building campaigns, nature projects, and contests in schools, and the organization of 4-H Clubs, Boy and Girl Scouts, Camp Fire Clubs, and similar groups have been definitely beneficial to small birds. One direct practical effect has been the provision of suitable homes for certain hole-nesting species whose potential nesting sites have been limited by human interference. The intangible results have been perhaps of even greater importance. Such contests and programs provide a wholesome outlet for the natural energies of the youth, and the interest aroused helps to provide a suitable introduction to the wider fields of wildlife conservation, an increasingly vital need in this country.

Birds of Prey

Harmful species, or those so labeled, may be injurious from restricted viewpoints or may even be so classed on erroneous information. A good example of the latter classification can be found in the general and widespread condemnation of hawks and owls. It is true that birds of this group kill poultry and to some extent prey upon game birds or animals that man wants for his own use. Some species are condemned by many ornithologists because of their destruction of small seed- and insect-eating birds, although it is doubtful that such a simple formula is applicable to the relationship between hawks and small birds. Under present conditions particularly, when small birds are well protected and hawks and owls of all kinds are held down by crusades and campaigns against them, it seems impossible that predacious species can destroy enough small birds to have any effect on the total breeding populations that survive.

Most species of hawks and owls feed largely on rodents, certainly not a harmful activity in an agricultural community, and from that standpoint alone it would be better to protect than to persecute them. Recent studies seem to indicate with increasing clarity that predation by hawks and owls has no noticeable effect on the breeding stocks of the game birds or animals that live in suitable environments. Despite this increasing evidence, some of which has long been known, the age-old attitude toward birds of prey still persists. Single individual observations and stories repeated until they have become almost traditional still guide much of the thought and action affecting these birds.

Based on present information, these birds as a group do little or no harm to forms in which man has a direct or indirect interest but rather are his allies in his warfare on rodents. Efforts expended against them, therefore, might well be used in more constructive conservation measures.

Crop-Destroying Birds

Fruit-eating and grain-eating species of birds are sometimes destructive to cultivated crops. Damage great enough to justify expenditures of time or money in control or prevention is usually traceable to one of several conditions: (1) Great colonies of birds may nest in close proximity to lands growing agricultural crops on which they may feed; (2) great migratory flocks may invade a district at a critical time in the crop season; or (3) crops may be so attractive to birds that they cause local concentrations sufficiently large to do them real damage.

The huge colonies of blackbirds that nest close to the fields of barley, rice, and other grains in the central valleys of California furnish a good example of the first condition. Serious losses are somewhat common during the nesting season, despite the large expenditure of effort and funds in preventive measures.

The former destructive attacks of bobolinks on the rice crops in states along the south Atlantic coast are well-known cases of the second category. Even such migrating game birds as ducks, geese, coots, and others occasionally do considerable damage to grain and other crops, and there are occasional authentic instances of damage by a wide variety of migrating nongame birds.

The local concentrations of fruit-eating birds when the crop is ripening in orchards in California and in other fruit districts well illustrate the third category.

Many of the problems raised are baffling in the extreme and require serious efforts for their solution. Pure biological reasoning will not solve the economic and social problems involved in cases of damage. Men dependent on crops for their livelihood cannot be expected to stand by and allow their margin of profit for a season's work to be wiped out by birds that theoretically may at other seasons be valuable as insect destroyers. It must be borne in mind that it is not necessary either for an entire crop or for a major part of it to be destroyed to have serious consequences to the farmer who is dependent on that crop. Margins of profit are usually slight, and it is on the profit rather than on the size of the crop that the grower depends. Such losses are visible and real to those concerned and must be given due consideration.

Small Mammals

The rodent family provides some of the most beautiful and interesting of small animals (e.g., kangaroo rats and tree squirrels) and some of the most repulsive (e.g., the Norway or brown rat).

Many of the small native mammals, including those otherwise valuable as fur producers, have characteristics that make them seriously destructive when brought into close proximity to agricultural crops. Careful studies have also shown a similarly destructive rôle in some circumstances by certain species that inhabit range and pasture lands as well. Most of these small mammals that are potential pests have several things in common. Feeding on the roots, vegetative parts, or seeds of plants, they readily turn their attention to crops when opportunity offers; they reproduce rapidly; and those of major importance occupy extensive ranges.

The great rodent family, which furnishes food for many wildlife forms and provides man with sport, food, and apparel, also includes the majority of the small mammals classed as pests. Troublesome in some situations, squirrels and rabbits are also considered game species, and beavers and muskrats are two of the most valuable fur bearers. Many species of mice, ground squirrels, prairie dogs, pocket gophers, and others are at times so destructive to crops that efforts to prevent or reduce the losses caused by them are very necessary.

Rodents of these groups interfere with man's interests in other ways than crop destruction. Their burrowing activities not only help to work and mix the soil but at times start destructive erosion gullies. Sometimes these accelerate destructive erosion, and on other occasions they seem to help check it. Whichever change takes place depends, among other factors, upon the type of soil, the slope, and the amount and season of rainfall. The burrowing activities of muskrats, pocket gophers, and ground squirrels have been known to cause breaks in dikes that store or distribute irrigation waters. Rodents act as forest planters by burying seed, some of which is never recovered, but they also at times are numerous enough to eat up the seed crop and so to prevent, or at least to delay, natural reforestation.

Last but not least, rodent populations provide a permanent reservoir of diseases readily transmissible to man. Among the most serious of these are bubonic plague, tularemia, and spotted fever. The reduction of rodent populations is one recognized method of preventing not only the spread of such diseases to other rodents, but also their actual or threatened outbreaks in man.

Dealing with Harmful Species

An attempt has been made here to show the ways in which nongame species regarded as harmful may affect man and his interests and to outline the fact that an intelligent handling of wildlife may involve problems in reducing as well as increasing the abundance. The solution of these problems may require control as well as restoration measures. That this is the case has been abundantly demonstrated in recent years with such beautiful and valuable species as deer and elk, and the same principle applies to the nongame forms. There has been much criticism of efforts to solve the problems associated with the management of these species but little effort on the part of the critics to find better solutions. In the following paragraphs little more can be done than outline the possible ways of attacking the problem. The methods employable are grouped under the following headings: (1) biological control; (2) change in farming practices; (3) use of repellents; (4) employment of frightening devices; and (5) removal of animals causing damage.

Biological Control

Biological control is often advanced as the best solution of problems that are presented in handling injurious forms of wildlife. It has been successful sometimes against destructive foreign insects that have established themselves in this country. Parasites that naturally prey on such foreign insects in their native homes have been introduced and after establishing themselves have reduced the population of their destructive hosts and consequently the damage caused by them.

No instance of similar success in dealing with destructive mammals or birds is now known. The mongoose was introduced into some of the West Indies to combat Old World rats, which were overrunning the islands, and while it eliminated the rat plague, the mongoose became in turn as great a pest as the rats had been previously. In Australia for many years a condition has existed that would seem to offer opportunity for an experiment along this line. European hares released there many years ago spread rapidly and these aliens soon became a major pest, without native predators to be effective against them. To introduce the American coyote or some similar predator to combat them might result in exerting a great pressure on the rabbit population, but at the same time it would involve the grave danger that the ultimate effects on stock raising might be more disastrous than are the present rabbit troubles, for Australia is one of the major wool- and mutton-producing areas of the world. Probably few biologists would care to assume responsibility for the ultimate outcome of such an experiment.

The use of viruses or bacteria to spread disease among destructive animals is often advanced as a possibility in biological control. This method has been tested to some extent in Europe on rats and mice, but the spread of any disease virulent enough actually to reduce these rodent populations to low levels would be potentially dangerous to human life. The reduction of European hare populations in France and England, and later in Australia, by the use of *myxamitosis* was the first successful use of a disease against a mammal population. It caused a great reduction of population over wide areas and apparent complete local extirpation in many places. In some cases there has been later a local build-up of population, possibly from a few individuals resistant to the disease.

Change in Farming Practices

Changes in agricultural practices or in livestock-pasturing methods may involve abandonment entirely of the affected crop or industry, or a change in cultural methods or practices. The disappearance of rice as a commercial crop in the Carolinas solved the problem of bobolink attacks on the ripening grain, but such solutions on a grand scale are obviously out of the question.

It has been found that clean cultivation of orchards in contrast to raising heavy cover crops there greatly reduces mouse damage to fruit trees. Where it fits into other agricultural needs this is a good solution for the mouse-pest problem, but it cannot be followed in districts that need to have the humus and fertility returned to the soil by the cover crops or where such crops are necessary to prevent destructive erosion.

The use of varieties of rice maturing early enough to be harvested before the arrival of the migratory birds that feed on this grain has reduced the loss in some cases, and changes in harvesting and threshing methods, particularly those that shorten the period between cutting and threshing, have sometimes had similar effect. Reducing the numbers of livestock on an overgrazed area or removing the animals entirely is sometimes effective in range restoration, even where a large rodent population is present, but at other times it does not produce the desired results. Soil types, species of rodents present, types of vegetative growth, and the extent of overgrazing are among the variable factors that influence the results of such attempts to improve conditions on grazing lands.

Use of Repellents

In recent years repellents have been developed that are successful in reducing certain kinds of damage. Treatment of seed corn with coal tar has some value in reducing the loss caused by crows and other birds in newly planted fields, but the greatest use yet made of repellents is in protecting trees from rodent damage. Various repellent washes, sprays, and dips have been developed and used with considerable success in protecting seedling conifers against rodents. Some of these treatments furnish protection for a sufficient period to make their use economically feasible.

There has been a growing amount of research on repellents with some interesting results. Biologists working in this field believe that it offers a most promising method of control of damage by resident rodent populations.

Employment of Frightening Devices

The use of the scarecrow, familiar denizen of many a garden and field, was one of the earliest ways of frightening employed in the effort to prevent bird damage to crops. It is still of value in some cases, and there are many ingenious modifications that sometimes afford a measure of relief from bird depredations. Bird watching, in which children are employed to drive grain-eating birds from the field, is as old as grain growing itself. Modern improvements on the device have been successful in some cases in reducing losses. Platforms are built at intervals throughout the field, and standing on these elevated perches the bird watcher can see a large area of grain about him. As flocks of graminivorous birds settle into the ripening fields, he frightens them away by shots from a .22 rifle fired into the grain. One or two of the newer improvements in this type of control will illustrate the possibilities of further developments.

Considerable success has been attained in California truck-crop districts in protecting sprouting vegetable seed from wandering flocks of horned larks by using lath stakes, to the upper end of each of which a long streamer of paper or light cloth is attached. Spaced evenly over the field at the proper distance, these have often been quite effective. Flash guns, which at intervals produce simultaneously a loud explosion and a blinding flash, are used with varying success against birds that feed at night or in the early morning and late evening. When hung in or near the trees to be protected, these have been of some use against fruit-eating birds.

All these methods are comparatively expensive, but they do have value in cases where bird damage is limited to a short period. They have not been so successful against destructive mammals.

Removal of Animals Causing Damage

Removal of populations of destructive birds or mammals is the oldest known method of dealing with the crop-damage problem. All the methods previously mentioned may be looked upon as efforts to find a substitute for actual killing. From the standpoint of the agriculturalist the control motive is usually economic. The effort is to find a more successful or less costly method of holding the damage to a minimum. The biologist and the out-of-doors enthusiast are usually influenced by their interest in wildlife rather than in the farmer's problems.

Traps, guns, poisons, and gases are among the weapons man has used against destructive birds and mammals since he began to grow cultivated crops. All the methods yet devised have their limitations, although some have been improved in recent years. An ideal control method would be one cheap enough to be economically feasible, specific enough to control the destructive species without killing other forms, and simple enough for anyone to use with assurance of success. Needless to say, no such ideal method has yet been developed. To be economically feasible, the method adopted must cost in time and expense less than the damage that would result if no control were attempted. Where an extensive area is attacked by a species prolific enough to be a major pest, this usually, although there are exceptions, rules out guns and traps as possible methods of control. Poisons and gases are limited in their effectiveness by many physical conditions, by the habits and behavior of the destructive species, and by the type of crop to be protected.

As a rule, gases are useful only against the burrowing mammals, and all known types and methods of use are limited in value in reducing the losses occasioned by these species. They are generally most effective against rodents that make comparatively short and simple burrows, and they produce better results when the ground is moist rather than dry.

Poisons of different kinds and on various baits have been in use in this country for many years in combating rodents. The old formulas, worked out by rule-of-thumb methods, have been gradually displaced by more selective poisons that can be specific in their application. The general tendency in the research on control methods now is to reduce the strength of mixtures, and to use a bait material and a method of application that will approximate most closely the choice of food and the feeding habits of the animal to be controlled. As these methods are refined, the danger of any accidental poisoning of other species is reduced, certainly a result to be desired. There is now also a marked increase in the interest to develop some of the nonkilling methods of reducing the losses mentioned.

Populations of rodents that are prolific enough to constitute a major problem in agricultural districts can be quickly reduced to a

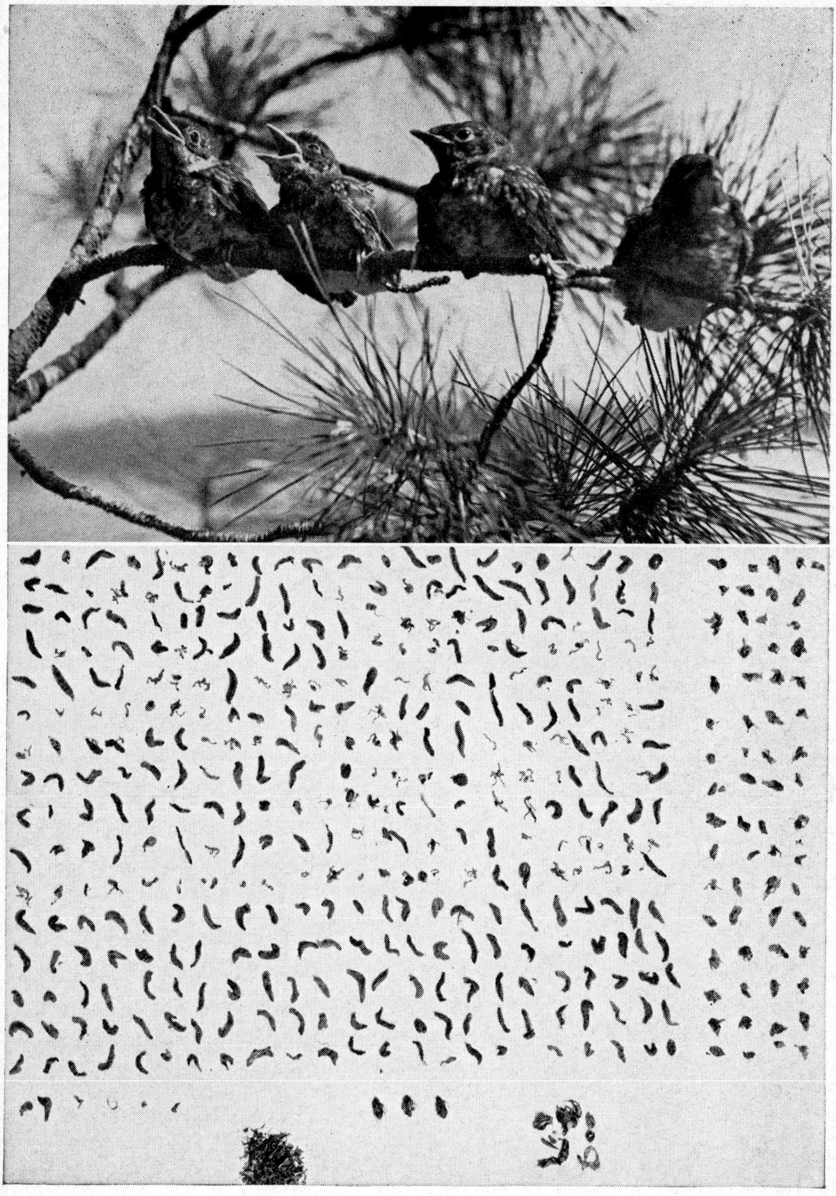

THEY ARE MORE THAN CUTE

Plate 25 / An appeal expressed by the handy word "cute," demonstrated by the young wood thrushes (above), explains the interest that many people take in bird protection; but farmers have an added interest, for they know that the insect-eating birds are also valuable enemies of crop pests: the stomach contents of a Brewer's blackbird (below) was found to include 442 alfalfa weevils.

(Fish and Wildlife Service photos: B48876 by R. D. Hildebrand; B598M, photographer unknown.)

A ROOM WITH BATH WILL DO

Plate 26 / Bird houses and bird baths attract many songbirds to the garden or lawn.

(Above, U. S. Department of Agriculture photo 5124C, photographer unknown. Below, Fish and Wildlife Service photos: B805M by F. E. Barker; B33316 by E. R. Kalmbach.)

OUR FAUNA INCLUDES MANY SMALL MAMMALS

Plate 27 / **Though less popular than birds, the small mammals also are interesting and important; their variety is illustrated by the skunk and chipmunk (above), the opossum (middle), and the badger and weasel (below).**

(Fish and Wildlife Service photos: B51645 by E. R. Kalmbach; B2816M by Francis Harper; B57451 by Wm. H. Schmidtman; B1321M, photographer unknown; B36965 by Almer P. Nelson.)

RODENTS ARE VEGETARIANS

Plate 28 / Living almost entirely on plant life, the pine mouse and prairie dog (above) come in conflict with man's interests, whereas the cottontail rabbit (below), in spite of its food habits, is valued as a popular game animal.

(Fish and Wildlife Service photos: B7965M by D. A. Spencer; B30129 by O. E. Stephl; B4677M by W. M. Rush.)

THE NATIONAL EMBLEM IS A HAWK

Plate 29 / The bald eagle, protected in the United States by Act of Congress as the National emblem—"symbol of the American ideals of freedom"—is a member of the hawk family and clearly illustrates the common characters of this group of birds.

(Fish and Wildlife Service photo B2998M, photographer unknown.)

OWLS ARE BENEFICIAL—ALL BUT ONE

Plate 30 / With the exception of the great horned owl, all owls in the United States are beneficial. Left to right: Above, young long-eared owls and young great gray owl; middle, barred and barn owls; below, burrowing and saw-whet owls.

(Fish and Wildlife Service photos: B977M by Ira N. Gabrielson; B24486 by Olaus J. Murie; B6408M by S. A. Grimes; B6775 by C. Hart Merriam; B949M by Ira N. Gabrielson; B57091 by George Tonkin.)

"THERE'S SO MUCH GOOD IN THE WORST"

Plate 31 / The smaller bobcat and coyote (above) and the larger wolf (not shown) and cougar (below) are the cats and dogs of American wildlife—predators generally condemned but found to be beneficial in some places when not too abundant.

(Fish and Wildlife Service photos: B34216f by L. J. Goldman; B56413 by W. M. Sharp; B2167M by N. W. McMillan.)

TRUMPETER AND WHOOPER MAY YET SURVIVE

Plate 32 / The trumpeter swan (above) and the whooping crane (below), among the tragic American wild creatures that are threatened with extinction, have in recent years increased on the Red Rock Lakes Refuge in Montana (above) and the Aransas Refuge in Texas (below). The national wildlife restoration program may still save these and other supposedly vanishing species.

(Fish and Wildlife Service photos: B56952 by Kenneth F. Roahen; B59489 by James O. Stevenson.)

certain point. Beyond that point reduction becomes slower and much more costly. Absolute extirpation of most of these species even from a limited area is far too costly to be considered from the economic standpoint alone. It has been attempted chiefly in dealing with outbreaks of rodent-borne diseases, and experience has shown that an area cleared of any of the rodents concerned can be kept free of them only by constant vigilance and effort.

The fact that as the rodent population becomes depleted the visible damage likewise declines, tends to cause cycles of rodent-control activity in any single agricultural area. As the damage declines the interest and activity of the landowners likewise diminish. As the population of rodents is built up, the damage again increases, and this eventually leads to another effort to reduce the losses.

Bird damage is, with rare exceptions, so irregular that systematic control efforts are not so much in evidence. In the case of both birds and mammals there are, of course, many other factors that enter into the highly complex problem of the relationships of some forms to each other and to economic interests. This chapter has been devoted to an outline only of the complexity of the control problem and to a discussion of some of the principal factors that enter into the natural rôles of useful and injurious nongame animals that prompt human efforts to increase or decrease their numbers according to man's real or apparent interest in them.

14 / Rare and Vanishing Species

Rare species of birds or mammals are those that either have never been abundant within our knowledge or have been so depleted in numbers that their existence is endangered. Such species as Kirtland's warbler, for example, are probably rare because of their special habitat requirements, not because of reduction in their numbers by direct human action. Those naturally rare may be limited in numbers by factors that are unknown or by conditions over which no human control can be effective. On the other hand, species that are known to have been abundant at one time but are now depleted by the action of man can be restored if man can correct the conditions he himself has produced. It is with this latter group that this chapter is concerned.

It would not help in discussing the problem to list the forms of wildlife known to be reduced to a danger level or to relate the history of species that have vanished. Rather an effort is made to point out the difficulties involved in restoring species now in a precarious condition and to discuss the rather limited tools that are available for the work.

To a biologist one of the greatest crimes of which man is capable is to permit the extermination of any form of wildlife. A species is a unique organism, one that has been produced by the action of natural forces through the ages and one that, when lost, is irreplaceable.

It will not mitigate the loss to reflect that geologic history records wholesale exterminations, by great cataclysmic or climatic changes or by causes unknown, not of species alone but of whole faunas. Moreover, there is no assurance that equally sweeping disasters will not again occur and bring about equally drastic changes in the chain of life, possibly even the destruction of the human race itself. If extinction does come it makes little difference whether a species is exterminated by geologic changes or by man, although the latter is resented because it is deemed preventable.

In evolutionary history it is entirely probable that species appear on the stage of life and develop an adaptability and variability that enables them to meet the more orderly changes in conditions. As they become old in a geologic sense, however, they gradually lose their adaptability and perish. According to general belief among biologists, successful groups, such as the sparrows among birds and the rodents among mammals, are comparatively recent lines that are now in the full flush of variation and adaptability. These, therefore, are represented by great numbers of species living under a wide variety of conditions.

There is geologic evidence, however, that some of the present mammals, birds, reptiles, amphibians, and fishes have survived from more ancient times and that although they once flourished in great variety, they now are represented by remnants only. Often irrevocably linked with special environment, they are more easily extirpated by locally varying conditions than are such species as the English sparrow and the house rat. The more adaptable and aggressive forms tend to spread and increase, while those that are more fixed in their habits and reactions may be limited to habitats that become ever more restricted as conditions change.

Causes of Extermination

Not only have geologic changes wiped out whole faunas, but man also has exterminated or contributed to the extinction of certain types of wildlife. There is little doubt that the passing of the great auk, the passenger pigeon, and the Eskimo curlew was due to the activities of man. The great auk disappeared as the result of raids by fishermen upon the few nesting islands that harbored the entire race. The passenger pigeon, a vulnerable colony-nesting bird, was unable to withstand the murderous hunting practices of the days when it was in its abundance and was reduced to a point where recovery was impossible. The Eskimo curlew was exterminated chiefly by market gunners.

Among the mammals, the near extinction within the United States of the grizzly bear is undoubtedly due solely to shooting. There have been no changes in much of its natural habitat and no factors capable of reducing it to its present low numbers other than man and his hunting activities. The practical disappearance of the sea otter—an animal that is now fortunately recovering under protection—was also due solely to human persecution. There has been no deterioration and little human invasion of much of its habitat, except for the express purpose of hunting the animal to obtain its valuable fur.

Reaction of Wildlife to Human Activities

The reduction in numbers of the upland plover and the long-billed curlew as nesting birds of the Great Plains was due to a combination of destroying their nesting grounds by grazing and plowing, and of overshooting them in this country and in their South American winter homes. The wood duck and the egret are examples of species that had become very scarce but have been restored by complete protection. Protection has a chance to restore wildlife where natural habitat remains available, but it cannot save species that no longer have suitable environment.

A striking example of differing reactions to protection is afforded by the two very similar swans found in North America. The whistling swan, with its nesting grounds in the far north largely undisturbed by man, has increased several fold in numbers since being put on the nongame list and given reasonable protection. Although the trumpeter swan, with a more southern breeding range affected by drought as well as by drainage and other human activities, had the same protection, nevertheless it long continued on the downgrade. Now, however, the trumpeter swan is gradually reinstating itself. Hunting was largely responsible for the decline in numbers of the whistling swan, which has recovered with protection, while habitat destruction and possibly lack of adaptability have added their part to the pressures that have slowed the recovery of the trumpeter.

A generation ago the egret, snowy heron, roseate spoonbill, and others had been brought to the verge of extinction by excessive killing for their plumage and to a lesser extent for food. Even reasonable protection, not always entirely enforceable, brought these birds back, sometimes in great numbers, and has increased also the numbers of such associated species as the limpkin and the white and glossy ibises. The restoration of these birds, with little change and certainly no improvement in their habitat, shows that shooting and commercialization were the prime causes of their decline in numbers. Habitat changes brought about by man are again reducing some of these species.

It is obvious from these few examples that there are various causes for the decline of species. To reverse the trend in some cases may bc impossible with present knowledge and means. On the other hand, there are threatened species that may be brought back by protective measures or environmental restoration, or both.

Some of the North American species of shorebirds that did increase as a result of the protection given them by the Migratory Bird Treaty Act, including the upland plover, Hudsonian curlew, black-bellied plover, and golden plover, are now menaced by a condition beyond control of the people on this continent. That condition is the development for agricultural purposes of their wintering grounds in South America. Increasing human occupancy of their wintering areas, particularly in Argentina, greatly complicates the problem of maintaining satisfactory populations of these birds, which are numbered among our breeding species.

Obstacles to Restoration

There are many obstacles confronting efforts to save and perpetuate the rare and vanishing species. It is quite possible that protective laws, no matter how rigidly enforced, will not suffice for the preservation of some of these species. More direct aid, by methods yet unknown, may have to be achieved to give these species a chance.

The trumpeter swan may again be presented as a good example. Its numbers are reduced to a few hundred individuals occurring in Canada in certain localities in British Columbia, and in this country in Alaska and in a series of small lakes in and adjoining Yellowstone Park in Wyoming, Montana, and Idaho. The most important of these lakes outside the Park are included in the Red Rock Lakes National Wildlife Refuge, a haven established by the Federal Government not only as a part of the general program for the restoration and development of waterfowl refuges, but also to help in the preservation of this magnificent species of bird. The Canadian colonies have been closely guarded by Dominion and Provincial authorities.

Both the National Park Service and the U. S. Fish and Wildlife Service maintain patrols in the United States to protect these birds. Although the final success of these efforts is not assured, gratifying increases have been made in the breeding stocks on the refuge areas within the United States and Canada.

When a species is so greatly reduced it is difficult to work out a restoration program, and there are so many doubtful factors that it is difficult to forecast the result. Coyotes get an occasional swan despite the utmost vigilance on the part of those trying to protect them. A number of the birds have injured themselves to the point of being unable to fly by beating their wings on newly formed ice. Several on the Red Rock Lakes Refuge have died from lead poisoning, and a number of those in British Columbia from undetermined causes. While the species was originally migratory, the remaining individuals are largely resident; perhaps they are remaining in winter under conditions they would better avoid. It may be that as marsh and lake restoration goes on some of these birds can be taken back to some of their ancestral nesting grounds that have not had breeding trumpeter swans for many years. These swans formerly bred as far south as Iowa and the Dakotas, although there are none now left in the prairie country. It is hoped that the birds can be restored, and one of the ways of accomplishing the purpose may prove to be scattering breeding stocks to eliminate the danger of destruction by local catastrophes.

Another angle of this problem is illustrated by the whooping crane, largest of its family on the North American continent and, like the trumpeter swan, a magnificent white bird that formerly bred as far south as Iowa and the Dakotas. The greater part of its nesting range also has been destroyed by agricultural developments in the prairie states and provinces. Survivors breed in remote marshes in Canada and winter almost entirely on the Texas coast, most of them occupying the Aransas Wildlife Refuge there. During their migration the birds usually stop over in certain areas of the Great Plains. It is no longer believed that in recent years shooting has been the determining factor in holding down the numbers of the wary whooping crane. In fact, its requirement of isolation and of vast marshes for nesting areas demonstrates that protection alone will not do much toward bringing it back. Attempts to restore the species are complicated by its migration over a territory extending 3,000 miles across the interior of the continent and by its spending large parts of the year in the widely separated summer and winter ranges. A marsh-restoration program, better protection by public sentiment, and more adequate law enforcement may combine to bring it back. Such a species, however, when reduced to a few individuals, is in a precarious situation.

As a third illustration, the ivory-billed woodpecker, a magnificent bird that formerly bred over the southern states from Texas north to Missouri and eastward along the Ohio and to North Carolina, is now probably extinct or represented by a very few individuals. It is quite probable that the diminution in its numbers is as much due to the destruction of its preferred habitat as to direct persecution. It is a bird of swampy forests of large trees—situations by no means so plentiful as formerly.

Complex Problems Involved

The grizzly bear may be cited as an example of a mammal that presents still other complications. The size and reputed ferocity of these magnificent beasts, together with their undoubted stock-destroying capacity, make it difficult to get public support for their preservation. Few state laws afford them protection, and they are fair game wherever sighted. The known survivors within the United States are confined mostly to Alaska, Wyoming, Montana, and Idaho, although there are a few scattered individuals in other states. British Columbia and Alaska harbor the greatest populations of these great bears. Even in national parks, where complete protection can be afforded and there are no herds of livestock to complicate matters, the problem of caring for such a wide-ranging animal is no easy matter. Outside the parks, sanctuary for the grizzly would be possible only if an area of suitable extent could be found from which stock grazing and human activity could be largely eliminated.

Other threatened species of mammals are the sea otter, marten, wolverine, and fisher, on whose heads a high price is placed because of the value of their fur. The value in itself has been the chief cause of their decline in numbers and is also one of the chief obstacles to their restoration, though there can be no question as to the desirability of restoring them.

The fur-seal herd offers an encouraging example of the restoration possibilities. The U. S. Fish and Wildlife Service, by following wise management practices, has increased this herd from a few hundred thousand to an approximation of the original Pribilof herds. This has been accomplished while the seals have produced a considerable revenue for the contracting parties to an international agreement that protects them on the high seas and permits the animals to be taken under supervision on the Pribilof Islands only. The entire story of this accomplishment of practical conservation is one to inspire hope for other wildlife resources.

Under careful supervision and protection by the U. S. Fish and Wildlife Service, the sea otter has been increased from a small remnant to a point where the harvest for fur of a portion of the annual increase soon may be justified. The problems in sea otter management are somewhat similar to those affecting the fur seal, but of chief importance would be patrol adequate to prevent poaching. There is no more promising field for practical wildlife conservation and management than the restoration of the animals that produce highly valuable fur.

Importance of Adequate Habitat

It must be obvious from the foregoing that the closed season, which is the first thought of conservationists, is not adequate in all cases. No closed season, no matter how vigorously enforced, could help the whooping crane or the ivory-billed woodpecker after their normal habitats were largely destroyed. Although both have had complete legal protection for years, neither has profited much by it. Homes must be assured for these birds and other methods of restoration must be developed and applied before species of this class can be increased. On the other hand, a well-enforced closed season, backed by adequate public support, can bring back species whose habitat is still unimpaired or at least approximates nearly enough its original form to be acceptable to the birds or mammals.

It is quite possible that some of the rare and vanishing species will disappear no matter how earnestly they are protected. They may have become so fixed in their requirements and reactions as to be entirely incapable of adapting themselves to present conditions. It does seem well worth the effort, however, if possible, to preserve them from extinction, brought about thoughtlessly or otherwise. Every species that vanishes from the woodland or prairie, or from the marshes or waters, leaves this country one less interesting natural feature and makes a gap that can never be quite filled by any other form. Conservationists will agree that conscientious and determined efforts should be made to protect the rare and vanishing species by closed seasons and by providing habitats where they will have a chance to restore themselves.

15 / Predator Relationships

No topic in the wildlife field is more controversial than that of predator relationships, and on none perhaps is there more loose thought and positive opinion based on insufficient consideration of the evidence that is available. The subject deserves consideration here because of its relationship to wildlife management rather than because of its importance in wildlife conservation.

Sportsmen, once they see a hawk kill a game bird, a crow steal quail egg, or a coyote destroy a deer or antelope fawn, are prone to regard these predators as monsters that on every one of the 365 days in the year are doing exactly what they have just seen and therefore as being a major factor in keeping down the population of the birds and animals that they wish to shoot. Relying upon fragmentary observations, many of these sportsmen thereupon promote "vermin"-control campaigns, many of which, to put it most charitably, are a waste not only of their own time and effort but also of an element of the native fauna. Very often the predator factor is not the one that is really responsible for a diminution in the numbers of a game species. Sportsmen therefore would do well to take some positive step to aid their favorites by discovering and attacking the real limiting factor or factors rather than by continuing useless efforts against the predators.

Even professional biologists have been misled in their appraisal of predator relationships. They sometimes exaggerate the importance of predators in suppressing destructive animals and often attribute to them hypothetical values in a manner that leads to their acceptance as facts. One statement frequently made is that predators render a useful service to game species in destroying sick and weak animals, thereby helping to maintain the vigor of the stock. There is not much definite evidence to substantiate such assertions, although they are widely advanced as a reason for the protection of predators.

Individuals interested in certain forms of wildlife also may become partisan and prejudiced in their judgment and deprecate the faults and glorify the virtues of favored forms. The extreme views among sportsmen, conservationists, and even biologists, on the subject of predator relationships, without a full weighing of the evidence, add to the vast problem of the interrelationships of all living forms. This relationship cannot be comprehended either by citing isolated individual experiences or by purely theoretical thinking on biological lines.

For example, enthusiastic bird conservationists are prone to exaggerate the value of the insect-eating habits of birds and their practical benefit to the human race. There is no question that the insectivorous birds on this continent consume enormous quantities of insects, and impressive figures showing the number or volume thus consumed, based on accurate measurements of stomach contents, can be quoted to show how many insects are destroyed in a given period by an individual bird or by the total population of birds on a certain area. Statements of this nature, coupled with the assertion that insects would entirely destroy the sources of human food if it were not for the birds, tend to present erroneous impressions that are not based entirely on fact. Entomologists generally consider that adverse climatic conditions, parasitic insects, and diseases are factors of more value in controlling insect populations than are birds, and they produce considerable evidence to support their position.

It is here impossible to go into all the ramifications of biological relationships, but some other phases that affect conservation activities may well be touched upon. In addition to bird predation on insects, there are certain other biological interrelationships that, directly affecting human interests, often occasion acrimonious discussion. These include the relationship of coyotes, wolves, mountain lions, bobcats, and other larger carnivores to the big-game and small-game species, and to domestic livestock; of fish-eating birds and fish-eating mammals to game fish largely (although predation on the commercial fishes is sometimes cited); and of predatory birds and small predatory mammals to poultry and to quails, grouse, turkeys, rabbits, squirrels, and other small game. Each of these relationships is complicated by its impingement upon human interests. After fifteen years spent in intensive work in predator-and rodent-control problems and on studies of the interrelationships of predatory and other forms, the writer confesses that he is much less certain in his idea of the significance of these relationships than he was before his biological theories had been tested by stubborn facts encountered in field experience.

Large Predators and Big Game

With the exception of the coyote, large predators are so few in number that under present conditions any possible effect that they may have on the total numbers of most big game is more theoretical than real. There are few places in the United States where mountain lions or wolves are now abundant enough to affect in any way the stocks of deer, elk, antelope, and other species of big game. The coyote is numerous enough in many sections to have an effect, though in most localities one that is not measurable by any practical standard. It is a fact generally observed by field workers that where there has been an abundance of coyotes or bobcats, a decrease in their numbers is frequently followed by a corresponding increase in the numbers of deer or antelopes. This is particularly true when the big-game population has been at low point. When the deer or antelope population is more numerous the effect of a decrease in predators is not easy to detect or measure accurately.

An outstanding example of the effect of predator control occurred with the upswing of the antelope herd in the territory adjoining the common boundary point of Nevada, Oregon, and California. In that region a small herd remained in 1920 and 1921, when the species had reached its lowest ebb there. The antelope were protected by state game laws, and there is little evidence that any considerable number were killed illegally. After their low point in 1920, when the animals had decreased noticeably from disease and possibly other causes, predator-control operations were undertaken by the Biological Survey, and between January 1, 1921, and June 30, 1934, a total of 7,595 coyotes and bobcats were removed. While this reduction of the predator population was being carried on, the antelope herds, which had for several years been stationary, with comparatively little success in rearing fawns, gradually increased from about 500 animals to a population of 7,000 to 8,000. This herd was numerous enough for the same or even greater predator pressure to be of less importance than formerly, and other factors affecting the herd have become more serious.

The general effect of predator control is so noticeable that whenever there is a reduction in the numbers of coyotes or bobcats in a territory where the deer or antelope populations are low but food and environment are favorable for big game, field workers expect an increase in the herds. Such conditions indicate that some factor or factors had reduced the herbivorous population below the carrying capacity of the range and that predator pressure was great enough to keep it at that point.

The coyote is a much more prolific breeder than these two big-game species and when their pressure is concentrated on the slower breeding forms during the fawning season it may have a definite effect on game abundance, even though there is no predation during the rest of the year. When the herbivorous population is high and predators are in normal numbers, predator pressure is obscured, and, to say the least, its measurement is difficult. Under such conditions predation may well become a negligible factor, and the predators, even though preying to a normal extent on deer or antelope, may still be utilizing animals that are surplus to the existence or even to the welfare of the herd.

Large Predators and Small Game

This same relation can often be observed in the predation of coyotes, bobcats, foxes, and other carnivores on rabbits, squirrels, and other small ground-inhabiting rodents. It is a common experience to find a large coyote population and a large rodent population side by side, both thriving, and no evidence of an undue repressive effect by the predators. This is probably the normal condition. The usual effect of rodent-control operations in such areas is to reduce the rodent population to a low level. If no further control is undertaken, recovery to former numbers takes place in three or four years, despite the presence of predators. This has been observed over and over again by many field workers.

A unique case has always interested me greatly. Intensive rodent-control operations in 1920 reduced the Oregon ground squirrel to a low level in an area almost entirely enclosed by high mountains. The physical barriers prevented any great influx of ground squirrels, and although conditions in this valley were observed carefully for a number of years, no appreciable increase in the local rodent population was ever observed. This was so contrary to the usual experience that it was noteworthy. Possibly the rodents were reduced to the point where natural hazards, including predatory enemies, kept them at a low level. Theoretically it is possible for a prolific species to be so reduced in a given area that it cannot recover in the face of normal natural hazards, but in practical experience such an occurrence is exceptional and not the rule.

Predators and Game Birds

There has been little research on the relationships of the larger predators to game birds. The numbers of mountain lions and wolves are so negligible in most of the United States that they could not appreciably affect small game-bird or mammal populations except locally. Such definite facts as are available indicate that while a predator will take game birds when opportunity offers, the number taken is seldom great enough to have any lasting effect. It is probably true that most predators will eat eggs and young birds at every opportunity. It is also true that a coyote, fox, or bobcat will take any bird that it can catch, whether young or adult. There is, however, little evidence that, if suitable food and cover exist and a normal bird population is present, the predator pressure is severe in the average territory, except under unusal weather conditions. Locally, conditions may be such that the predator pressure upon game birds is pronounced, but as a rule, it has not yet been demonstrated that inroads by these animals are a serious factor in reducing normal breeding populations.

Predator and Hunting Pressure on Game

Where game birds or mammals are subjected to severe hunting, the addition of the hunting pressure to other adverse factors may quickly reduce the normal population of game. In such areas predators may be a factor of importance, and their reduction may be necessary to a greater production of game. Some contend that the predators have as much right to the game as do the human hunters. Others assert that human interests are paramount. There is much controversy over these conflicting viewpoints, though in actual practice the direct human interest in increased food or game supplies usually wins out and control is undertaken to reduce the predator population and the pressure on the game species. Under such conditions, to determine whether predators shall be allowed to harvest a part of the game crop or whether efforts shall be made to reserve as much of that part as possible for human use becomes a question of public policy.

Large Predators and Livestock

Predatory animals sometimes seriously affect range and farm livestock. While it is undoubtedly true that grizzly bears, for example, are so scarce and local in distribution that their effect on the livestock industry as a whole is negligible, yet an individual grizzly that has learned to prey upon livestock might threaten the prosperity of the particular stockman whose herds it attacks. The same can safely be said of the mountain lion and the wolf. The number of sheep, cattle, and poultry killed by these animals in the United States as a whole is a very small fraction of the total production; yet the unfortunately situated individual producer may have all of his profit wiped out by the depredations of one or more of these animals upon his flocks and herds. Eliminating these predators of restricted numbers and distribution leaves only two predators that are of practical importance to the livestock and poultry producers—the coyote and, to a much less extent, the wildcat.

In favorable range the coyote is often abundant enough to be seriously destructive to sheep and poultry. Of all native predators it is the one most able to take care of itself and, in the face of intense persecution, one that has steadily extended its range. Many explanations have been advanced to account for this spread, including the elimination of the timber wolf, which has been supposed to have kept it out of the higher mountain country. The removal of timber and the conversion of many forested areas to brushlands, pastures, and farms, with increased production of small farm stock, undoubtedly created favorable environment for the coyote, and facilitated its spread. Control operations have always been carried on against this animal either by the individual effort of those affected or in a general way by means of bounties or organized drives. Nevertheless, the coyote still holds its own in many parts of the country. Only in a few major stock-producing areas, in which the losses are heavy enough to justify unremitting control, have its numbers been held in check.

It should be pointed out that coyotes live largely on rodents, and that because of local conditions many individual coyotes have no opportunity to destroy any form of poultry or livestock. On the other hand, a single animal may become exceedingly destructive and cause great losses to the poultry or stock raiser. If the losses caused by the present coyote population could be spread over the entire livestock-producing areas of the United States so that they would not fall heavily upon any one individual stockman, they could probably be borne without calling for control. In fact, however, losses are always more or less concentrated in definite areas, and sometimes may be great enough to put small operators out of business or to wipe out the profits of some of the larger ones.

Small Predators and Small Ground-Inhabiting Birds and Mammals

A class of predators more widely distributed than the large carnivores and, because of their greater abundance and close association with their prey, of greater importance, especially on farms, includes hawks, owls, crows, weasels, and skunks, as well as locally minks, turtles, foxes, and others. These animals sometimes encroach upon the real or imagined welfare of other creatures in which man is interested. Farm poultry losses from these species are local and sporadic, though often severe upon individual flocks. They occur frequently enough to give the species a bad name. When losses from these mammals or birds occur, they are used as an additional argument to justify control on the grounds of their supposed interference with the production of a greater quantity of huntable game, including rabbits, squirrels, quails, grouse, wild turkeys, and wild ducks. To many sportsmen every individual predator is a deadly rival for the supply of game. Locally, some do prey rather heavily upon game species, but that is not the same as saying that they reduce below normal the abundance of the animals preyed upon.

Kalmbach's studies in Canada, where for two years he found 31 per cent of the clutches of duck eggs destroyed by crows, is a case in point. As Kalmbach himself points out, he had no evidence to show how many of the 31 per cent would have grown to maturity if the crows had not taken them—possibly none would have—as the normal loss of eggs and young of many kinds of birds reaches 60 per cent or even more. On the other hand, studies by the same biologist on the Lower Souris National Wildlife Refuge in North

Dakota showed that the crow, though present in numbers, took only a negligible proportion of the duck eggs and that there the skunk was the chief predator. These findings do not mean that crows everywhere take a third of the duck eggs; neither does it indicate that wherever they fail to take such a toll skunks replace them as enemies. In other areas snakes take a considerable toll. Again, the cotton rat was found by Stoddard to be one of the chief enemies of the quail in restricted areas.

Errington's comprehensive studies in Wisconsin and Iowa indicate that winter depredations on quails by predators are not a serious matter where food and cover are adequate. Winter food and cover apparently influence survival capacity, and predation rarely reduces the birds below that survival level. If, however, quails on a given area enter the winter season with two or three times the population that can safely be carried, predation may cause heavy losses. Errington observed, however, that if before the winter was over, this population had not been reduced to the carrying capacity of the land by predators, it would have been by other factors. Under such conditions, the loss by predation, therefore, is more apparent than real.

Stoddard found in the marsh hawk a valuable ally to man in suppressing cotton rats, which in his study area proved to be one of the chief enemies of the quail.

All in all, the evidence tends to show that under local conditions one or more of these predators may become noticeably effective against certain kinds of prey, but these local findings are not a true guide to the effect of predators on total populations of game over large areas. The safer assumption is that the effect, instead of being more than the proportions indicated by certain special studies, is less, and certainly much less than the average sportsman believes.

It might be pointed out that in only a small fraction of the breeding range of migratory waterfowl are wild ducks found nesting in close proximity to the crow, which is one of the chief objects of the sportsmen's wrath, and crow predation on these game species is confined to the breeding season; therefore, crows cannot possibly have the great adverse effect upon the continental duck population that is alleged. Many careful studies of the relationship of predators and small-animal populations indicate that predation is not the major limiting factor upon the total populations of these species. In almost every case investigators have ranked predation as subordinate among suppressive agencies. Shortage of food, dearth of cover, incorrect relationship of food and cover, and disease are all more potent factors in limiting desirable animal populations than is predation.

John and Frank Craighead, as a result of an intensive study of the relations of hawks and owls to prey species, believe that these predators do exercise a repressive and perhaps at times controlling effect on meadow mice and other small rodents.

There are areas where predation is important enough to justify control activities. It is well to keep in mind, however, that there is much evidence that if every predator upon grouse, quails, ducks, or any other desirable form of bird or mammal could be exterminated, it still would not bring back the happy days when there was plenty of game for everyone wishing to shoot.

The relationship of these small predators, particularly mammals, is further discussed in the chapter on fur-bearing animals.

Fish-Eating Birds

The destruction of fishes is another much discussed phase of predation. Forms accused of destroying game fishes are otters, minks, and raccoons, among the smaller mammals; and herons, grebes, loons, mergansers, kingfishers, and pelicans, among water birds.

Careful studies in both field and laboratory have failed to substantiate claims that predation is as serious a source of loss of edible and game fishes as is often claimed. These views come largely from sport fishermen, although occasionally the commercial fishermen manifest an interest in some phase of the problem. Among both classes, the usual formula for estimating damage is the same as in the case of small-game predation. A fisherman sees a merganser, a loon, or some other predator taking a fish—say a perch or a trout. Immediately he begins to figure on the pounds per day of fish it will take to keep the bird alive and assumes that it spends every day of the year catching the fishes in which he is interested, and estimates an appalling total loss of fishes to a comparatively small population of fish-eating birds. Such calculations are wide of the mark.

Many studies prove that while the accused birds do eat fishes, they get far more of the rough and nongame varieties than of the game fishes. This is only natural, for the less prized species are the more common in most waters. Further, fish-eating birds consume many snakes, frogs, crustaceans, and insects, some of which also are destroyers of fishes. Mergansers, loons, and grebes stick more closely to a fish diet than do herons, terns, and gulls, although even these supposedly entirely fish-eating birds vary their diet with crawfishes and other small crustaceans, amphibians, and insects. The examination of thousands of stomachs and other studies indicate that fish-eating birds as a whole are not a great factor in the destruction of game fishes. The proportion of food and game fishes taken is low in comparison with the rough fishes and the miscellaneous items taken.

The economics of "trash" fish, a term often applied to species not utilized for food or sport, are not unequivocal. Some of these fishes are spawn eaters and destroy the small fry of game fishes, among others; from that aspect, their destruction by fish-eating birds may be more beneficial than harmful. Many of them, however, are also food for the adult game fishes, and hence it might be argued that the fish-eating birds enter into direct competition with the game fishes for food. Some of the birds themselves eat spawn, again complicating the situation. At hatcheries and places where fishes are confined in small feeding and rearing ponds, losses by fish-eating birds may be very serious, and under such conditions control or protection may be fully justified.

Local concentrations of fish-eating birds may have a serious adverse effect on the populations of desirable fishes. Mergansers have been most frequently named in such local problems, although other species are also involved on occasion. Concentrations of fishes by adverse water or other conditions sometimes result in their depletion through depredations of concentrations of fish-eating species attracted by them.

The general realization that many warm water game fish reproduce so prolifically that they produce stunted populations of thousands of individuals too small to be of any value has effectively removed any justification for control of fish-eating birds and mammals from such waters. Some fishery workers studying trout and salmon find that mergansers do take quantities of small fish from certain streams; however, the effect of this predation has not been determined.

This country has long since passed the point where natural production of trout can meet the demands for sport fishing. Many streams and lakes, especially those near large cities, are so heavily fished that it is becoming the common practice for state game and fish commissioners to stock them continually through the fishing season with legal-sized fish. Fish-eating birds had nothing to do with the shortage this practice endeavors to overcome, and it is entirely probable that the energies now directed against fish-eating birds would be more productive of permanent good to sportsmen's interests if spent in attempting to stop the pollution of the streams, cleaning up those already polluted, and in improving the general condition of the waters.

Views on the Need for Predator Control

There has been much discussion of the underlying philosophy of predator-control operations and the need for them. General control participated in by state and Federal Governments has been justified largely on the ground that the Federal Government owns 50 per cent or more of the land area in most of the western states, where the great range livestock industry is conducted, and that it is unjust to expect individual owners or groups of owners controlling only a fraction of the vast land areas to handle the predatory-animal problem unaided. It is also argued that supervised control, with all its faults, is more selective and therefore less wasteful of other forms of wildlife than is control by individual effort.

Some contend that coyotes are so valuable as rodent destroyers that they could well be left alone in the interests of the stockmen themselves. It is difficult, however, to convince many livestock operators or farmers of the validity of this theory when they see the profits of their work taken by the raids of predators. They see a tangible loss, and if rodent repression by predators has any economic benefit it is so intangible as not to be evident to those who must view the practical side. Moreover, it must be admitted that no one has yet shown definitely a practical control of rodent populations by predator activities. The distinction should be kept in mind between natural balance in a natural world, where the only question may be the survival of prey species, and the degree of control of losses that is necessary to economic success where human livelihood is involved. To achieve the latter, direct action by man usually is required, whether the control problem is that of reducing losses from insects or plant diseases or from mammals or birds.

On the basis of stomach analyses it is easy to calculate the number of rodents that a coyote might eat during a normal lifetime. It is equally easy to reach an astronomical figure in calculating the number of rodents taken by the total coyote population in a year. This, however, would not in any way convince the man who suffers direct loss of livestock from the depredations of coyotes that he is the gainer by their destruction of rodents. A coyote may live largely on rodents for a number of months, then invade a poultry yard, a flock of turkeys, or a band of sheep and in a short time do so much damage as to outweigh any good it may have accomplished by eating rodents in the previous months.

The practical side of this matter is that there is a definite loss to the livestock industry, usually felt most severely by the small operator, and that this loss is direct and visible and very frequently a serious matter to the individual concerned. It is inevitable that some sort of human control will be exerted, but a compromise between extremists as to the proper degree and scope is difficult to arrange. Sane handling of the problem obviously lies somewhere between the total extermination desired by the outraged stockman and the no-control ideal of the detached nature lover.

It is always to be kept in mind that the destructive effect of the predation here discussed is not so much upon the total population of domestic animals as upon the economic welfare of human beings dependent upon those populations. For example, coyote activities might never completely destroy or even greatly reduce any certain band of sheep or flock of turkeys, and yet they might seriously affect the livelihood of the families dependent upon them. The margin of profit, which must furnish that livelihood, is usually small and a very modest loss may wipe that out.

In such circumstances the problem becomes not one merely of animal interrelationships but of economics and human economic welfare as well. So long as it is necessary for man to tend his flocks in regions seriously infested by predators, some form of control will be exercised. Theorizing as to natural balance of animal populations in the world will not change the fact. The real questions are, how much control is necessary and how shall it be undertaken? On both these questions there is much room for argument. A fair examination of this phase of the wildlife problem makes it obvious that control is necessary in some areas and that in others no control is justified. There is also a borderline zone between the two where differences of opinion will always occur between the advocates of drastic control and those believing in little or no control.

Principles of Predator Relationships

The subject of the ramifications of predator relationships is much more intricate and varied in any community than could be indicated in a brief discussion, but an attempt has been made to outline in this chapter some of the chief complexities. To remedy some of the difficulties obviously will require more study, especially more accurate determination of the effect of predation on animal populations. Such information, where available, may completely change present concepts of this very complicated problem. There has, however, been sufficient research and practical experience in these problems to warrant the following tentative outline of a few basic principles of predator relationships:

1. Under normal conditions over a wide range, predators generally live upon surplus populations of prey species and their activities in the aggregate have little or no effect upon the breeding stock needed for the succeeding season. Local readjustments in accordance with varying conditions are often desirable to maintain a balance, though this can never be perfect; the observed *average* stability of animal populations emphasizes this point.

2. Under special conditions, either favorable to the predator or unfavorable to the prey, predators may become a real factor in decreasing populations or in preventing recovery following a decline in population.

3. The effect of predation upon populations is more evident when the predator is a more prolific species than the prey. Where the reverse is true, the effect is at least obscured by the fact that the victim has a greater reproductive capacity than the predator.

4. Generally the agency of predators in reducing large populations is minor compared with the more vital one of available food, the supply of suitable cover, the correct interspersion of these two essentials, and disease. Any one of these, or factors unknown, may be more effective than predation in limiting numbers.

5. Human interests, primarily economic, will always be paramount, and when predation on domestic animals is involved it is useless to explain it from the purely biological point of view. If domestic-animal populations alone were concerned, predation on herds or flocks might not result in a serious or abnormal decrease, but the economic factors involved and the sociological effects preclude a purely biological approach to the problem.

6. The numerical ratio of game animals and game birds to their natural predators may be disturbed when human hunters enter the field. Utilization of the game crop by man, therefore, may necessitate some reduction in numbers of predatory species, if a supply of game is to be maintained.

16 / Wildlife Refuges and Their Place in Conservation

Wildlife refuges may be defined as areas of land, or of land and water, that are set aside and managed definitely for the protection and preservation of one or more species of the native fauna. They may be, and often are, correlated with other uses that do not conflict with their chief objectives. Whether established by public or by private agencies, they are frequently and increasingly correlated with land-management programs undertaken primarily for other conservation purposes.

Areas thus reserved are important tools in wildlife conservation even though they do not provide a perfect solution for all conservation problems. When properly selected and administered, however, they insure the perpetuation of breeding stocks of the animals they seek to protect.

Refuges may vary in size from a few acres to vast stretches of country, depending upon the habits of the species involved. To fulfill their purpose, however, they must provide adequate food and cover for the period during which they are used. For resident species, year-long needs must be provided; whereas it may be necessary to care for migratory forms during only a short season at any one point.

Refuges may be discussed under the following four headings: (1)

Big-game refuges; (2) refuges for small resident game; (3) waterfowl refuges; and (4) refuges for colonial nongame birds. On the ground there is often no such clearcut distinction between refuges as can be drawn on paper. Every refuge for migratory birds provides sanctuary for resident species, and conversely those established and managed primarily for residents may furnish food, cover, and resting places for some of the migrants.

Big-Game Refuges

The big-game refuges now in existence vary from small sanctuary areas, where a few individuals may find safety from the hunters' guns and thus preserve a breeding stock for the territory, to huge areas for the preservation of populations that are or have been in the past threatened with extinction. Good examples of the latter type are provided by some of the great national wildlife refuges, such as Hart Mountain (Oregon) and Charles Sheldon (Nevada) for antelope; and the Desert Game Range (Nevada) and Kofa Mountain and Cabeza Prieta (both in Arizona), for remnant bands of bighorn sheep. All have been planned to insure the perpetuation of species under natural conditions.

After refuges for big game have been established, the first management efforts are usually directed toward increasing their populations. If these efforts are successful, a new set of problems may arise. Experience with big-game refuges has shown that deer, elk, and other browsing or grazing species under protection on restricted areas may build up populations to a point where they take the food supply to an extent that brings about starvation. Under conditions that prevail in the range of these animals, the destruction of forage often first seriously affects the food supply in winter, when it is frequently more limited than that available during summer and fall.

At one time it was a widely accepted belief that establishing and adequately patrolling huge refuges was the only step necessary to preserve a species. The necessity of management was ignored, a mistake that soon became evident. On areas where no hunting whatever is allowed, the surpluses of buffaloes, elk, and other big-game species must be regularly removed in order to hold the herds down to the point where they will not actually destroy the range. The animals may be disposed of by slaughter, used for restocking other areas, or given to parks and zoos. In any event, the biologically significant fact is that animals have to be removed from protected ranges in order to prevent range destruction. Permanent big-game areas must be carefully managed to limit the numbers of animals, just as livestock is limited to the carrying capacity of a farm; or they may be small enough for the animals to spread out to nonprotected territory. The latter principle has been used successfully in Pennsylvania, the surplus being partially harvested by hunters.

Where populations of deer and elk have acquired a breeding momentum, hunting pressure often is not great enough to stop the increase even under relaxed hunting regulations. Special measures have then been found necessary. The removal of excess big-game animals by methods other than hunting is expensive and except in the case of controlled herds in fenced enclosures it has not been very successful. The Kaibab deer herd is the classic example of a population built up to the point where all measures tried failed to remove the surplus in time to save the browse plants. Starvation of large numbers of deer resulted, and the carrying capacity of the range will be impaired for many years. Populations of browsing animals on protected range can be maintained only by restricting their numbers to the carrying capacity of the range and many big game refuges have been reduced in size or abolished completely as the game herds have increased.

Refuges for Small Resident Game

Small refuges, as a means of preserving portions of the breeding stocks of upland game birds, were developed and used by many states. The basic concept behind this program was that of utilizing

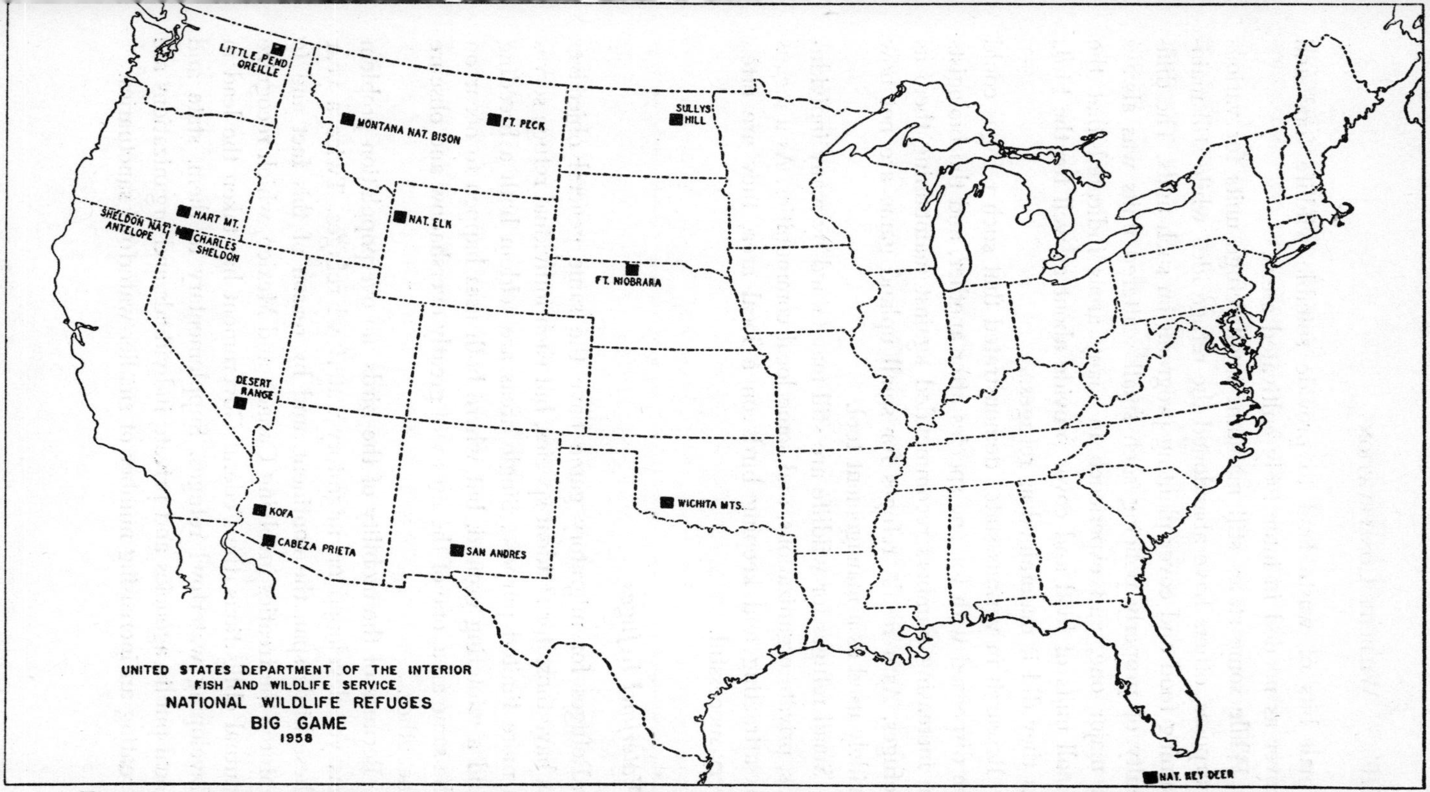

Fig. 14 / National wildlife refuges for big game, administered by the Fish and Wildlife Service of the U.S. Department of the Interior.

small bits of waste land to provide suitable wildlife food and cover as needed in intensively cultivated areas.

While some states still maintain small refuge units for various purposes, others have abandoned the refuge idea while still maintaining food and cover planting programs on such units. The difficulty of properly policing such small scattered units was always a major one, and experience in many areas indicated that the small units of food and cover provide about as well for the birds as they did if maintained as refuges.

Research in various states demonstrated that such refuges could be dispensed with for one species after another, and the biologists in increasing numbers recommended against maintaining them as refuges. As a result, refuges for small upland game are not now widely used as a management tool.

Small refuges for wildlife are still maintained by many individuals, private organizations, and some local communities. As a means of attracting and keeping birds on a local area, they are often very successful.

Waterfowl Refuges

Refuges for migratory game have the same general objectives as have those for resident species, but each individual refuge serves a more limited purpose. Single areas are seldom both a breeding and a wintering ground, but where both uses happen to occur on the same area, one of the uses will greatly overshadow and obscure the other.

Because of the mobility of the birds, no overpopulation problem has yet developed on migratory-waterfowl refuges. Twice a year these birds span the continent, and by reason of this fact and to enforce the treaties involving Canada and Mexico, which recognize mutual obligations, the Federal Government has taken the lead in developing waterfowl refuges. Supplementary to them, state and local public agencies and private individuals and organizations are creating an increasing number of smaller waterfowl sanctuaries.

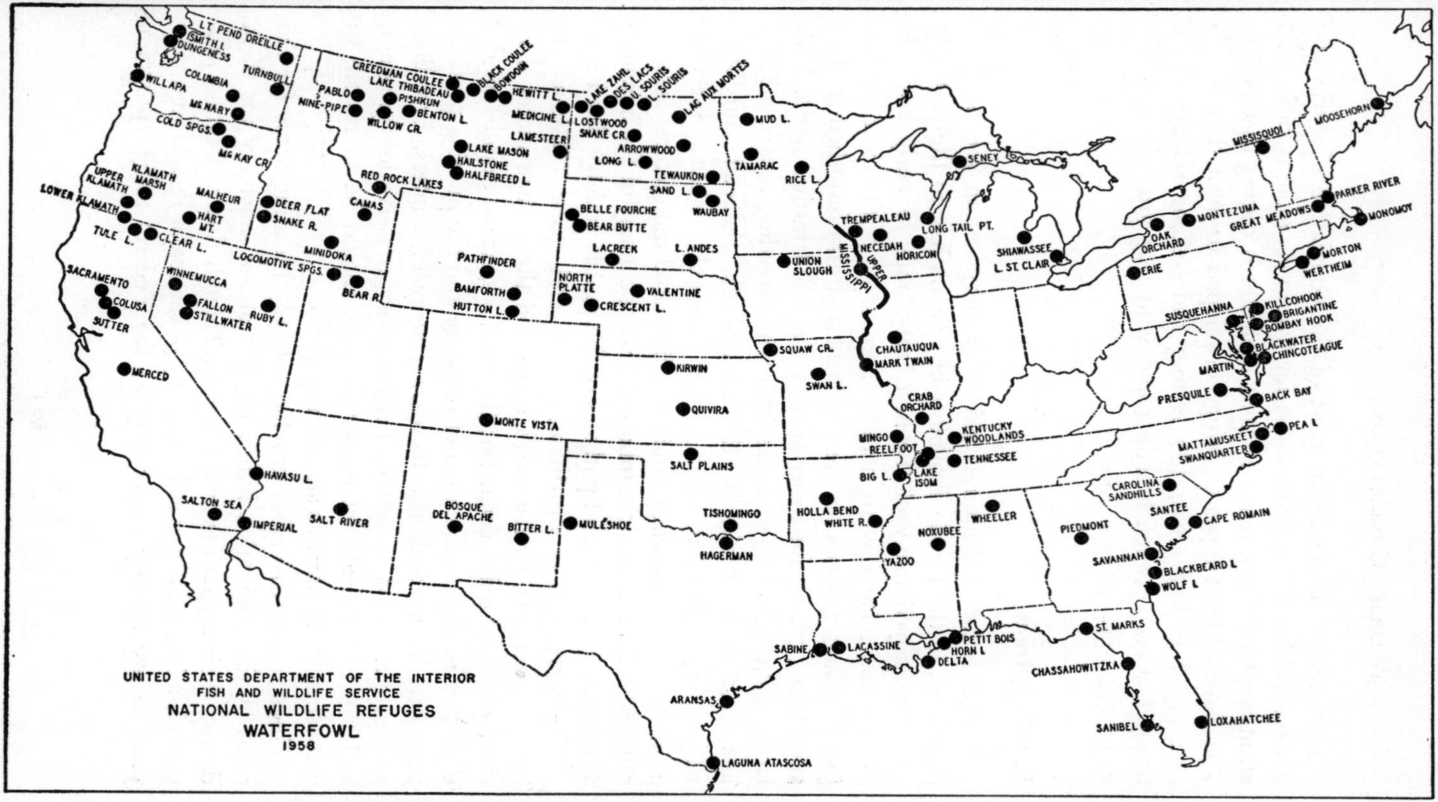

Fig. 15 / **National wildlife refuges for waterfowl, administered by the Fish and Wildlife Service of the U.S. Department of the Interior.**

Recognizing the fact that most of the population of ducks and geese is within the United States for five to six months each year, an attempt has been made to meet their needs during that period. The three distinct types of refuge developed to meet these needs are: (1) breeding areas; (2) resting and feeding refuges along major flyways between breeding and wintering grounds; and (3) wintering areas.

Breeding Areas

Drainage for agricultural and other purposes in the northern states and in the Prairie Provinces of Canada has, in the past fifty years, destroyed many of the best marshlands formerly available to waterfowl. These were, acre for acre, some of the most productive breeding grounds on the continent and also furnished feeding and resting places for many species that bred farther north. Mallards, pintails, and other ducks with wide breeding ranges suffered less than such species as the canvasback, redhead and blue-winged and cinnamon teals, which formerly enjoyed breeding grounds in the area where drainage eliminated the greatest acreage of marshes. When drought followed drainage, many of the innumerable marshes, ponds, and potholes of the prairie country dried up.

The more widely distributed ducks and geese continued to breed extensively farther north and stood the change better than the more localized species, but the total waterfowl population declined under the combination of drainage and the hunting pressure produced by a constantly increasing army of hunters. Breeding-ground restoration is part of the necessary conservation program, and the ultimate aim of conservationists should be to restore to waterfowl every possible acre of marshland.

These restored marshes provide not only breeding areas for the birds as the population builds up, but also a sanctuary for them during their migrations twice a year. Though this restoration program is a long-time one at best, many of the major restorations now possible are already under way in the Federal refuge program.

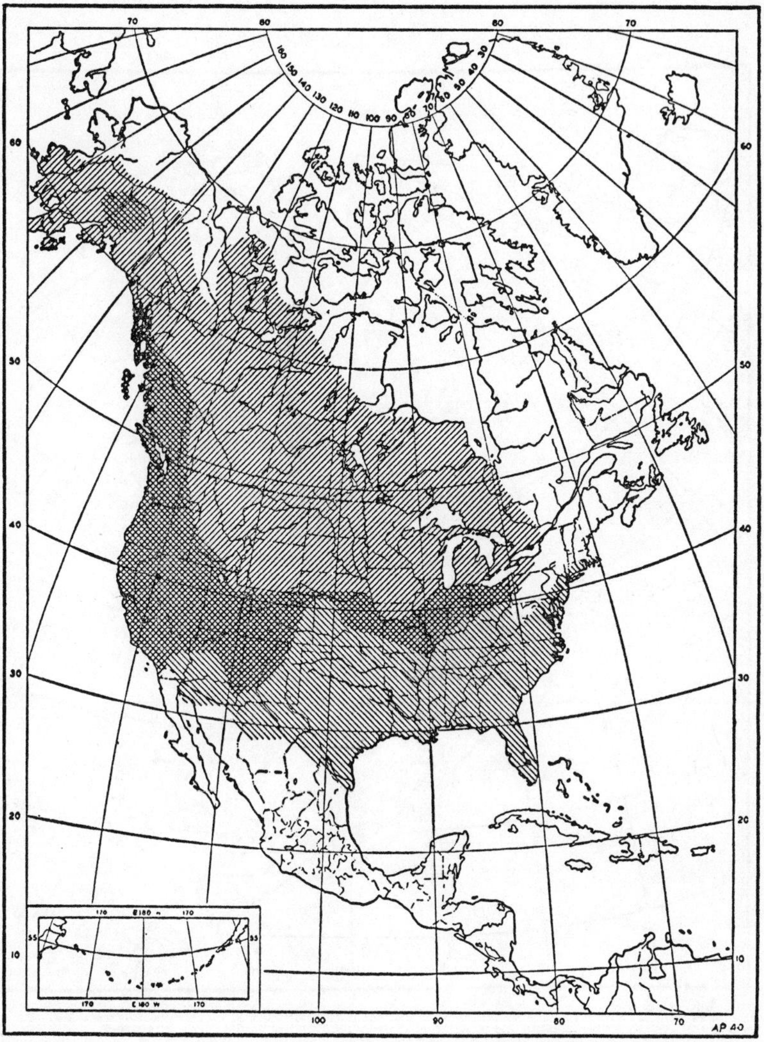

Fig. 16 / The crosshatched and more northerly shaded areas show the breeding range of the mallard; the crosshatched and more southerly shaded areas, the wintering range. In crosshatched areas these extensive ranges overlap.

Fig. 17 / Canvasback regions. The stippled areas show the principal breeding range of the canvasback; the other shaded areas indicate the wintering range (after Stewart, 1958).

Fig. 18 / The crosshatched and more northerly shaded areas show the breeding range of the blue-winged teal; the crosshatched and more southerly shaded areas, the wintering range. This is one of the few North American ducks that regularly go to Central and South America in winter. Comparatively small numbers remain on the south Atlantic and Gulf coasts during that season. On the Gulf coast, chiefly in Louisiana, and on the eastern shore of Maryland two small nesting areas overlap the winter range.

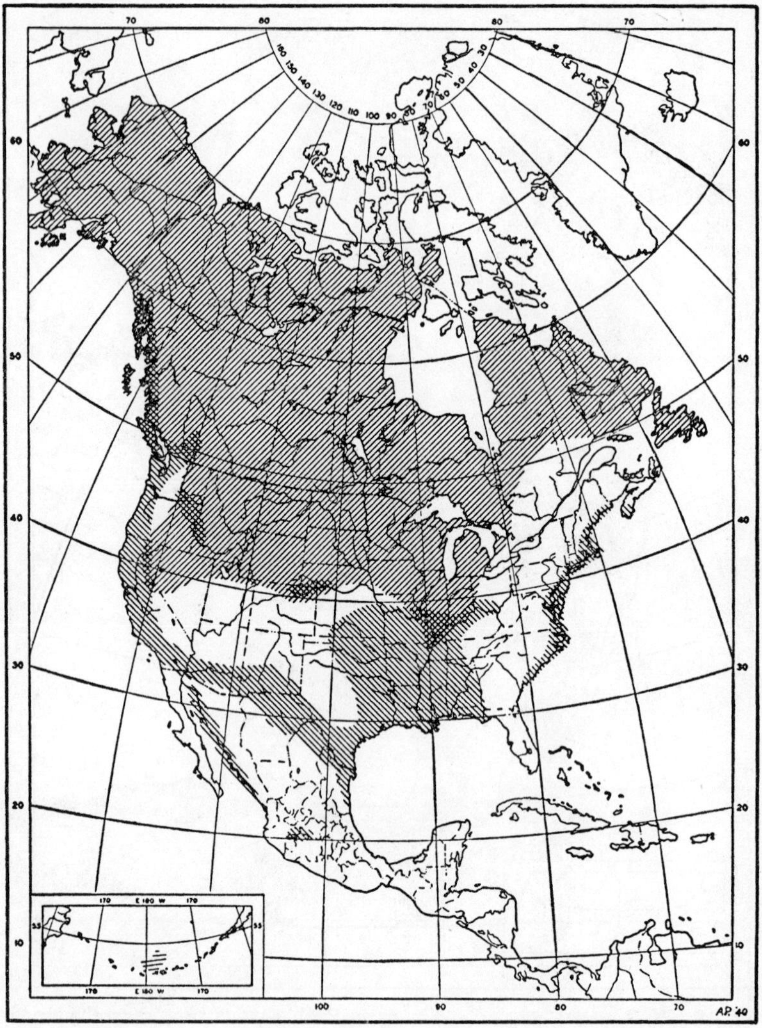

Fig. 19 / **The crosshatched and more northerly shaded areas show the very extensive breeding range of the Canada goose; the crosshatched and more southerly shaded areas, the concentrated wintering range. In crosshatched areas, the ranges overlap. The most important wintering grounds are on the middle Atlantic and Texas coasts and in the lower Mississippi and interior California valleys.**

Fig. 20 / The shaded northern areas, almost entirely north of the Arctic Circle, show the breeding range of the whistling swan; the other shaded areas, the wintering range. The most important winter quarters are on the coast of Maryland, Virginia, and North Carolina and in California.

The thousands of additional smaller lakes, ponds, and marshes which can be restored with benefit to the communities in which they are situated, offer one of the greatest opportunities in the wildlife-conservation field for local action. Such smaller areas,

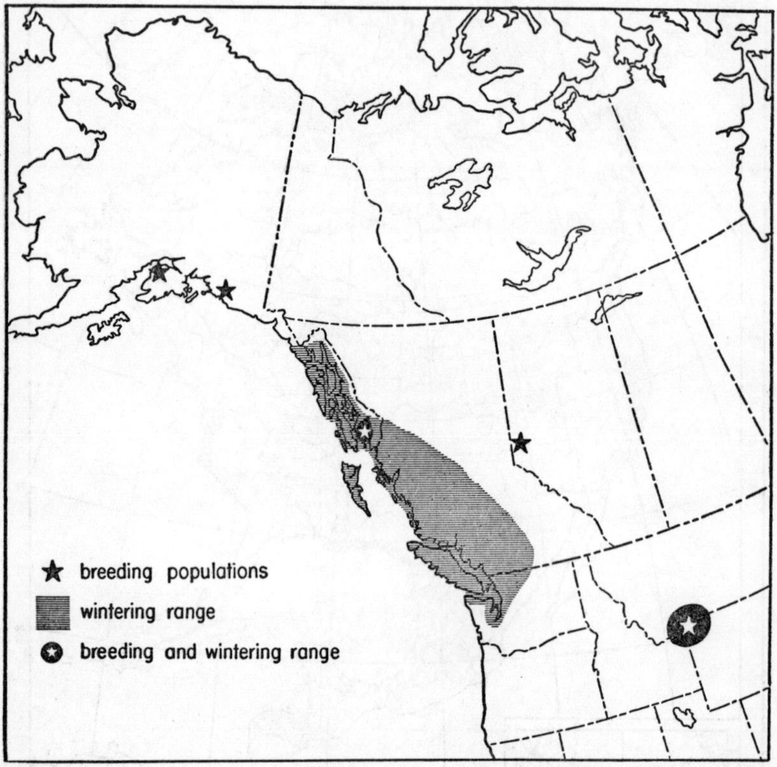

Fig. 21 / The present principal breeding and wintering ranges of the trumpeter swan (after Banko, 1959).

whether refuges or not, will produce fishes, waterfowl, and fur. They will also contribute to the restoration of water tables, help regulate the run-off, and aid in the program for the prevention of soil erosion. At the same time they will admirably supplement the larger marsh-restoration program of the Federal Government.

Flyway Refuges

Flyway refuges are smaller and lie in a broad band east and west across the country between the breeding areas to the north and the wintering grounds of the south. A few pairs of birds may remain on any of them to breed, and in some years wintering birds may remain. The principal purpose of such refuges, however, is to furnish food and water to the birds as they travel, as well as a resting place and safety from too much hunting pressure. Therefore, they should be so managed as to produce the maximum supply of natural food. There should be one or more of them in each major concentration area, and the ultimate objective is to have them spaced not more than 100 miles apart in each of the four principal flyways. Such areas may vary in size from 3,000 to 25,000 acres or more, depending on the local possibilities rather than on any fixed rule. Suitable sites are more difficult to locate and often present more complicated development and management problems than do the breeding areas, where relatively simple stabilization of water levels often is possible. They are, however, an essential part of the refuge program.

Wintering Grounds

Sanctuary for an adequate part of the bird population and the assurance of food for the winter months, when the continental stock of waterfowl is concentrated within narrow limits, are essential parts of any refuge program designed to perpetuate these birds. Refuges in wintering areas are often large, and, like the flyways refuges, are managed so as to produce the maximum of food for the use of the birds at the proper season. On an ideal breeding marsh, the desired maximum water level should be attained in May and be maintained well into August, and even after that period it should not drop too low, lest the marsh vegetation, which must provide food and cover for next year's crop of birds, deteriorate unduly.

Fig. 22 / Principal wintering grounds of North American waterfowl. The most important of these are on the south Atlantic and Gulf coasts and in the lower Mississippi Valley. The solid line indicates the northern winter limit except for the areas in British Columbia and Alaska that are occupied in mild seasons.

On flyway refuges and wintering grounds the water levels can often be drawn down to advantage in May or June, after which smartweed, chufa, barnyard millet, and similar foods can be produced. To be of maximum value, it should be possible to raise water levels enough to flood such food areas in September or October as the birds move southward.

Refuges for Colonial Nongame Birds

Refuges largely for nongame species, consisting usually of small islands along the coastal waters or in the larger lakes, often protect colony-nesting birds, including gulls, terns, murres, puffins, cormorants, auklets, and murrelets. These species tend to remain year after year on the spot and require little from man save freedom from molestation. Such reservations have been successful in protecting these breeding colonies and allowing them to grow to considerable size—in some cases to their maximum capacity.

Less successful have been rookery sites set aside for herons, pelicans, and certain other birds that periodically move from one nesting area to another. These birds habitually leave protected for entirely unprotected nesting sites without warning, their moves being correlated with changes in the food supply or polluted conditions at the rookery. Some observations tend to show that ammonia in the bird droppings may kill the vegetation and thus cause a move to an area where the birds can be in leafy trees rather than among bare branches exposed to the direct rays of the sun. Incidentally, the first national wildlife refuge was established to protect a colony of brown pelicans on the Florida coast—Pelican Island, set aside by President Theodore Roosevelt on March 14, 1903.

In addition to these smaller refuges set aside under the Federal system chiefly for colonial nongame species, there are numerous others maintained by states, local communities, private organizations, and individuals. Some are to protect certain colonies or areas, others to furnish general wildlife havens. A number of cities have lakes in their city parks, where waterfowl are attracted by heavy

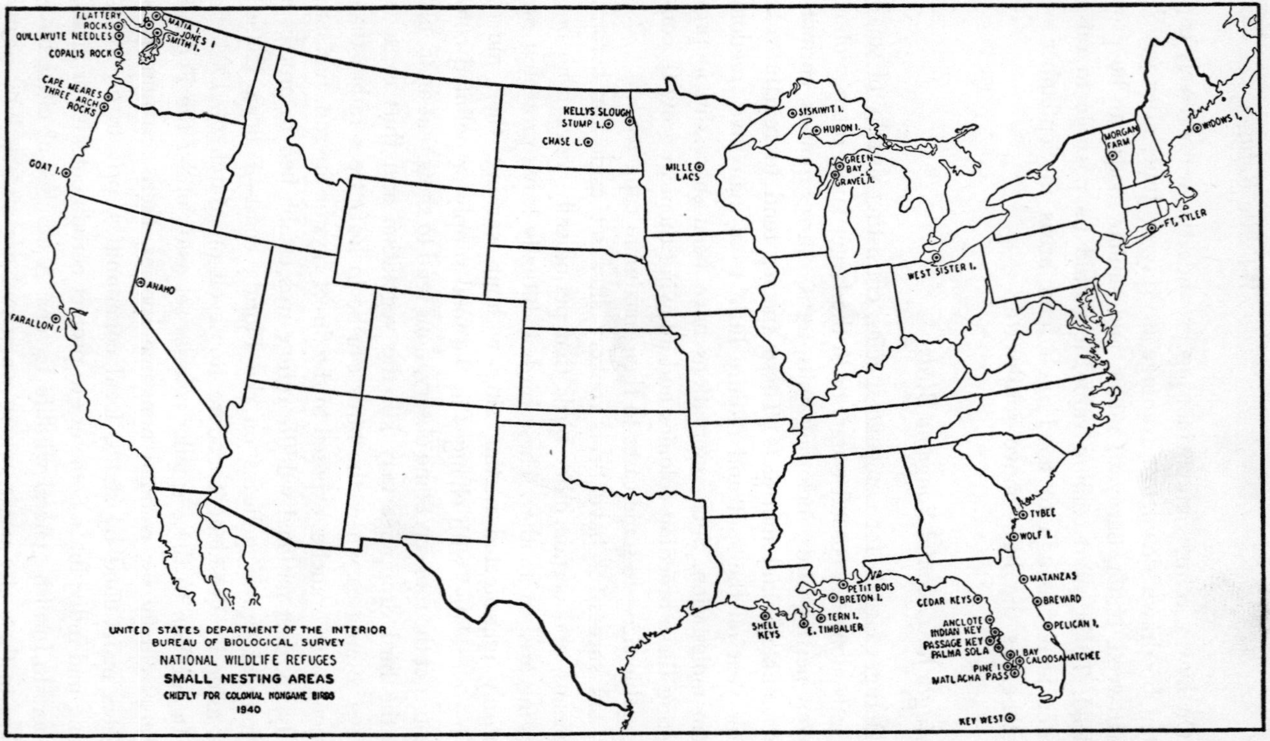

Fig. 23 / National wildlife refuges which provide small nesting areas, chiefly for colonial nongame birds, administered by the U.S. Department of the Interior.

feeding. Lake Merritt, in Oakland, Calif., is one of the best known of these, although there are now many others that not only save the birds but also serve a great educational purpose in interesting the general public in wildlife and its perpetuation. Each refuge, regardless of its particular purpose, serves as a haven not only for its own form of wildlife but also for innumerable others. Some birds and small mammals quickly avail themselves of any improvement of food and cover conditions brought about by good management.

Marshes restored primarily for waterfowl furnish food and shelter for many upland species about their margins, and the very fact that marshes have been restored has resulted in the establishment of thriving colonies of marsh and aquatic birds in districts from which they had long been absent. Malheur Lake, in Oregon, soon after its restoration attracted back to its wide expanses every species of bird that was known to nest there prior to its destruction, and restored areas in Montana and the Dakotas have been restocked with thriving colonies of grebes, terns, gulls, herons, shorebirds, and other aquatic birds.

The National Wildlife-Refuge Program

The Federal marsh- and lake-restoration program is based on the sound conservation principle that suitable environment must be provided if waterfowl are to be maintained. Within the continental United States it is of first importance that an adequate breeding stock of birds be preserved. The provision of adequate refuges in the proper places is the most certain way of accomplishing this purpose.

The acquisition and development of 12,500,000 acres of marsh has been determined to be the minimum likely to accomplish that result. Not just any 12,500,000 acres will do. It must be distributed in such manner as to furnish protection to the birds of each flyway and also to groups within those flyways that are accustomed to wintering, resting, or breeding in certain areas. With present continental populations of birds these areas have been determined and about half the program is completed or is under way. Its completion is essential for the long-time program of management that must be applied if these birds are to be restored and maintained as a valuable resource.

At present there are about 200 Federal refuges completed or under purchase and development primarily for waterfowl in the United States, totaling almost 3,500,000 acres. Of this number, 65 totaling 94,856 acres, are small easement nesting refuges. In addition there are about 500,000 acres of marsh and water on general wildlife refuges that are of some use to waterfowl. It is estimated that about 5,000,000 acres of state marsh areas will be needed to supplement the Federal program. Many states are vigorously pursuing a marshland acquisition and development program. As a result, so many areas are being developed that any tabulation would soon be out of date.

Changing Character of Refuge Terrain

Refuges are suitable for a given species or group of species if the right combination of plants is present. If, however, plant conditions change—for example, if grassland gives way to trees—it will be to the disadvantage of some forms of wildlife and advantageous to others. Such changes may drive some species entirely out of an area or cause shifts from one part of a refuge to another. However suitable a refuge may have been at the time it was established, it can become less valuable for any definite purpose unless managed to maintain favorable conditions.

The whole progress of geologic erosion—of the sorting, shifting, and rebuilding of soils, as described in an earlier chapter—brings with it great and often surprisingly swift changes in local ecology. A snowslide may sweep a strip of forest off the land, and entirely alter not only the appearance but also the kind and quality of the food and cover produced. Floods, by moving soil from one spot and depositing it in another, may destroy an ecological type in one place and start a different one at some other.

The fact that on all land and water there exists a definite succession of life cannot be altered by making some areas sanctuaries. These successions may be swift or slow, widespread or limited, depending upon the present state of fertility, water supply, climate, and many other factors.

On land with sufficient rainfall, herbaceous vegetation tends to be replaced by bushes, and bushes by trees, through a succession that may extend over a century or more. During this long period the area becomes more favorable for some and less favorable for other groups of birds and mammals, according to the type of habitat developed, and the only way in which these changes can be prevented is by artificial interruption. This is seen to happen as a result of lumbering operations.

The water succession is less obvious; but lakes silt up to become marshes; marshes gradually become drier and shallower by the growth and decay of vegetation and through the deposition of silt brought in by erosion of the watershed, and at length they become meadowlands. Streams cut back to lakes and drain them, leaving basins that may be marshy or not, depending on the thoroughness of the drainage. In many cases it has been necessary to put in artificial dams to prevent erosion from lowering lake levels and to build dikes in order to restore lake levels and to re-create the conditions desired. Such changes in both water and land make it difficult to devise a refuge system that will be adequate for all time.

For the present, refuges can be fitted into other land-use programs and are being so fitted to an increasing degree. Flood-control works, navigation, erection of dams, power developments, and reclamation projects whose primary purpose is to irrigate farmlands, can often be made to serve the additional purpose of wildlife restoration with little interference with their primary objects; and conversely, much of the refuge program has a value in contributing to soil conservation, flood control, and reforestation. Recognition of these possibilities is much more general than formerly, but there is still a great field for coördination to the advantage of all concerned.

Summary

To summarize, refuges have a definite place in the conservation field. Their principal function is to preserve wildlife. Each may be created for any one of numerous objectives, but usually it contributes to the welfare of other species than those for which established.

Refuge alone cannot solve the problem of restoring wildlife populations. They can, however, often assure a continued breeding stock from which restorations can be made.

Refuges for browsing and grazing animals must be carefully managed. If not, their very success in increasing wildlife may operate to destroy the food formerly available to the favored species.

Refuges for migratory waterfowl are indispensable to any sane management of this resource. If numerous enough, properly placed, and correctly managed, they provide a more or less automatic safety factor for breeding stock.

Many small refuges are still needed to provide the same local factor of safety that the larger units do on a national scale.

Research is essential to wise management of refuge lands if their character is to be preserved so that they may function to serve not only the present but also future generations of wildlife.

17 / Surmounting the Obstacles to Conservation

It is so obviously in the national interest to care for and use wisely the natural resources of soil, water, forest, grasslands, and wildlife, that it would seem a simple matter to establish and maintain a good conservation program. The contrary, however, is the case. From the preceding chapters it is seen that any national program for the conservation of wildlife and of other natural resources involved presents many exceedingly complex problems, the solutions of which are not now, and probably never will be, fully known. Only within recent years have technicians themselves come to realize the close relationships of the various phases of conservation, and such appreciation by no means extends to the general public. To be convinced that this is true, one has only to listen to some of the popular radio-quiz programs to learn how few people know the answer to any question dealing with conservation, compared with the number who promptly answer queries about the latest movie stars, orchestra leaders, or other popular celebrities.

The lack of public understanding in itself indicates that there are still obstacles, and great ones, to be overcome before conservation can become an established American social practice.

The basic difficulties that must be surmounted may be grouped under three headings: (1) The shortsightedness of the human race;

(2) the tendency to seek panaceas rather than real remedies; and (3) the lack of knowledge and understanding.

Shortsightedness

Mention need be made of only a few of the things that have been and still are being done, to demonstrate that shortsightedness is one of the fundamental obstacles to the adoption of conservation practices. Lack of sufficient consideration is everywhere evident in the promotion of local enterprises that, on the surface, may seem beneficial but that, with study, could have been recognized as detrimental both to local and to national interests. The country is so full of these characteristically American undertakings that it is unnecessary to do more than mention them. Drainage ditches and barge canals have often destroyed marshes, when a little care and planning at the time of construction would have prevented the loss of these valuable areas. Again stream-straightening enterprises may help a few people locally but be a great detriment to the people farther down the waterway. Drainage for mosquito control has often been pushed far beyond any actual demonstrable needs without due consideration for other values damaged or destroyed.

Stream pollution, either by industrial plants or by communities, is a striking example of national shortsightedness. Immediate convenience or temporary benefits are allowed to obscure probable long-time disadvantages. Only too often do we see that the community suffers, often permanently, by loss of vitally needed pure water and the destruction of other values that streams and lakes might produce, such as fishing, boating, bathing, and other recreational facilities. It has not been uncommon in American experience to permit streams to be ruined by pollution and then to spend lavishly to provide artificial recreational areas to replace those that had once been naturally available. Satisfactory methods of handling wastes are known, and allowing a beautiful stream to be converted into a sewer cannot be justified on the ground that a temporary financial advantage accrues to a community or industry. Stream pollution is not in the public interest and should be prohibited by public policy. The importance of keeping streams pure and available for uses definitely in the public interest is so well established that it is almost incredible that wasteful pollution should still be permitted and that new sources of pollution should be contemplated with complacency.

The drainage of marshes and lakes, which has been of benefit chiefly to the promoters, is still being practiced, although on a reduced scale. It is not implied that there is no drainage that might possibly be for the good of the people locally or of the nation. It is fair to point out, however, that locally promoted enterprises often do not take into consideration the factors that make for permanent good. To be of real benefit, drainage should provide uses and values greater than those it destroys. Many drainage schemes that are promoted result in loss of the water resources and the products of these waters without compensatory return. Soils made available by drainage are often unfit for sustained agricultural or other uses. Careful studies of all phases of such drainage proposals by unbiased technicians who have no financial or other interest in the project should always precede action, and construction should be undertaken only in those that are certain to be assets rather than liabilities.

Forest destruction in America, either by individuals or by great corporations, is another example of shortsightedness. Europe has learned by hard experience to manage its forests better. When timber is cut, it is replaced. In this country there is too little replacement except by public agencies, and reforestation has not kept pace with timber cutting.

An obstacle to the proper handling and utilization of wildlife is often found in the attitude of hunters and fishermen who desire to take more game or fish than the crop available for harvest, regardless of the condition of the breeding stock. Harvesting should be based on accurate knowledge of stock, and human memory in such matters is notoriously undependable. The failure to remember accurately conditions in years gone by is demonstrated each year by requests for changes in shooting regulations based only on the last year's experience rather than the average record over a period of years. Often two groups in the same community will make requests for radically different seasons, based solely on the memory of their shooting luck a year ago. Such requests are often utterly selfish in that those who make them do so in the desire to get something for their own group regardless of the effect upon others. It is too common, not only among those who hunt and fish but among others dealing with natural resources, in the abstract to be all for conservation and wise use but in practice to be only for self at the other fellow's expense.

Jealousy between communities is another illustration of shortsightedness in dealing with wildlife conservation problems. A good example of this is the deplorable condition that has prevailed for many years with respect to the fishes of the Great Lakes. Even after those making a livelihood out of the commercial fisheries realized that the supply was being rapidly depleted, the hope of each group or community of getting advantage by postponing remedial action has prevented any improvement. Illustrations of human shortsightedness thwarting conservation could be extended almost indefinitely, but the foregoing should serve to prove the point.

Seeking Panaceas

The second great obstacle to conservation is the constant tendency of the human race to seek a superficially promising way out of difficulties rather than to face the facts and undertake drastic remedies. A striking example of panacea seeking has been the construction of levees to handle the flood waters of the Mississippi. These do protect local communities, but they do nothing to check at the source the constantly increasing menace of floods. Not only are such floods much more destructive than formerly, because of the encroachment of human habitation on the lowlands, which formerly were flooded by the river without doing great damage, but also because the rivers are constantly being forced into narrower channels by levees and dikes, despite the obvious risk in forcing a greater and greater volume of water through a constantly decreasing channel. The inception of floods has been everywhere increased by the stripping of the forests from the headwaters, the draining of the lower lakes and marshes, and the use of unwise agricultural practices, all of which have combined to hasten the run-off and increase the volume of water in the main streams at critical times.

The fields of hunting and fishing furnish two very popular illustrations of the tendency to take the easiest way out rather than seek basic solutions of conservation problems. As the wildlife population decreased in this country, the first conservation effort was to restrict the take. While this is still a very necessary tool in wildlife administration, it is not a sovereign remedy for all the ills that beset us. For many years it was generally felt, and some people still feel, that a restriction on the utilization of wildlife species is all that is necessary to bring back the good old days, but restriction is not constructive and will not replace other measures. When it became obvious that this was true, there was a great development of artificial propagation and distribution. This program, which is still going on on a large scale, may be helpful under certain circumstances, but it does not furnish a complete solution of the problem of maintaining game stocks. There is a growing if belated recognition of this fact.

The other popular scapegoat for the continual decline of wildlife utilized for sport has been the destructiveness of predatory species, or so-called "vermin." In correction of this fallacy, however, it is necessary only to point out that in the good old days that so many look back upon as perfection or near perfection, predators existed probably in much greater numbers than at present. "Vermin" are still a very popular scapegoat, particularly in the view of many sporting magazines and sporting clubs. Nevertheless, it is certain that killing all the predators would not solve the problem of maintaining the demanded supply of sport species in the face of the pressure that is exerted against them by hunters and fishermen and by continually restricting the environment.

The latest attack on the problem of supplying huntable game, and one that is being widely attempted, is restoration of environment. The time and effort spent in restoring food and cover in the right relationships will result in increased natural production indefinitely, if the take is so regulated as to safeguard the breeding stock. This undertaking is basically sound and, although it probably never can solve all maintenance problems and restore game species to the great numbers that formerly existed, it is the most hopeful development that has taken place in the field of game conservation.

Lack of continuity in wildlife programs is a defect that may be ascribed to a mixture of politics and panaceas. It particularly affects the efficiency of state agencies, which, because of their scope, have the greatest opportunities for initiating real wildlife conservation and utilization programs. With the exception of migratory birds, the wildlife of the nation is largely under state administration. All too frequently, however, the personnel, particularly the executive personnel, changes so often that there is little possibility of any wildlife-conservation program continuing long enough to demonstrate its usefulness. Incoming officials may feel it necessary to make spectacular innovations, regardless of the merits of work that may be thus disrupted. So long as governors are permitted to look upon the conservation funds and organizations as material for building personal political machines, this difficulty will persist.

Lack of Understanding

A great part of the public is indifferent to the success of wildlife conservation, feeling that it has as its chief object the provision of targets for the guns and of fish for the lures. Official agencies are at least partially responsible for this feeling, which traces to the fact that conservation agencies often depend for their financial support upon fees for hunting and fishing, and that, therefore, they feel responsible for their acts to those who hunt or fish rather than to all the people. Such an unfortunate narrowing of the wildlife program results in a corresponding limitation of public interest and understanding.

Conversely, many who hunt and fish feel that they have a greater interest in the out-of-doors than those who do not, and a proprietary right in the wildlife of forest and stream. As a rule, they do manifest interest in wildlife, for when there is any crisis, such as a severe storm that renders unavailable the food supply for local game birds or mammals, those who hunt or fish are the ones who respond most quickly to the emergency and who help with either food or effort to see that the brood stocks for the next year do not perish. There is, however, a steady public feeding and protection of all kinds of wildlife that can be attracted to the vicinity of homes. This is not undertaken by sportsmen alone nor does it wait for crises, but it benefits some of the favorite game groups, as quails, rabbits, and squirrels, and it is safe to say that it is done at a great percentage of the homesteads of the nation.

The greater right of those who hunt or fish to dictate policies of wildlife conservation is widely questioned. Under American law and theory game and fish belong to the State—that is, to all the people. Those who hunt or fish pay license fees for the privilege of reducing to personal possession certain bits of this common property, but their fees give them no better title to the remaining stock than that of any other citizen. In practice, however, the interest of the license holders is manifested so much more than that of the average citizen that its effect on the policies and regulations for harvesting wildlife is much greater than is justified by the proportionate numbers of persons involved.

The history of American game conservation shows that sportsman influence can be harmful as well as beneficial. It has been injurious when groups have devoted their energies to fighting for greater harvesting privileges than the supply warranted, or to squabbling over details of regulation and administration. It has been beneficial where local leadership has been wise enough and strong enough to insist on the employment of competent administrative personnel and the development of careful plans for safeguarding and perpetuating wildlife.

Many of the wisest leaders of conservation have come from the ranks of sportsmen, but they were men who were able to look ahead and foresee the effects of the abuses to which wildlife resources were being subjected. It is also true, however, that most of the resistance to intelligent game-conservation programs has come from those who hunt and fish. These groups have had their way often enough for the trend in game and fish stocks to be for many years, on a national scale, with minor exceptions, pretty consistently downward. This spirit of resistance still prevails, and the adverse attitudes of groups of sportsmen are still too often a major factor in hampering conservation programs.

Lack of understanding also traces to the fact that most individuals are so absorbed in their own occupations or avocations that they fail to appreciate how important the conservation of natural resources may be to them individually, to their children, and to their children's children. Those who are not in direct contact with the out-of-doors, or directly dependent for their livelihood upon the land or the products of the land, usually give little thought to the basic value of natural resources in providing them with food, clothing, shelter, and other necessities of life.

Another indication of lack of understanding is found in the tendency of conservation groups to quarrel over details of conservation rather than to center their attention on its major aspects. This deplorable tendency can be observed in a meeting of almost any conservation group, where the time used in discussing unimportant details is likely to compare unfavorably with that devoted to consideration of the main problems before it. This certainly is a vital defect in our conservation activity. Many a fisherman's group will argue for hours over the daily limit or legal size of fish and never devote a moment to combating pollution of their favorite waters, even though that evil may even then be so far advanced as to threaten the elimination of all fish life.

Another thing that results in a lack of understanding is the paucity of basic facts. This is something that is being gradually remedied, but the research undertaken in this country has never yet been great enough to meet the needs of conservation in any of its phases. The ever-shifting pressures and changing economic and social needs are constantly creating new conservation problems and probably always will.

Remedies

The foregoing are by no means all the obstacles to progress in conservation but may be regarded as the most prevalent. How can these obstacles be overcome? There is no panacea, and no simple solution will ever be found; but six needs for which there are remedies may be suggested.

1. The greatest need is for an alert, intelligent conservation group in every community. Each group should challenge every project that will radically alter vegetative and water conditions in its section. Much needless damage may be averted if, in drainage projects, the construction of huge dams, the establishment of industries that increase pollution, the erection of new levees pushed closer to the river centers, or in great land-selling programs, those who promote the "developments" are forced to give consideration to all the probable results before the work is undertaken, and to render an accounting before the bar of public opinion. Vigilance in these respects will always be necessary. There will ever be grasping hands eager to despoil our basic resources, and there must be strong and resolute conservation forces to oppose and control the spoilers.

2. The next greatest need is to have more of the population understand conservation and to get it so fixed in their minds that it will become part of their philosophy of life. There is, after all, only one certain way to accomplish this, and that is by education in the schools and in various groups and associations, in fact, in every conceivable way. Conservation forces might make much more headway if, instead of arguing over details, they would devote their energies to seeing that the educational policy on conservation is

firmly established. Let the schoolmasters work out the pedagogical details, which to the conservationist are relatively unimportant. It makes little difference *how* it is done, if only it *is* done.

3. Persistency in the conservation movement is essential. Constant education and unremitting public pressure are needed to convince all concerned that no matter how far this country has succeeded in restoring its forests and wildlife and in conserving the productivity of its waters and the fertility of its soils, for all time to come it will be necessary to see that these resources are never again exploited to the point of destruction. On the average, only the annual increase should be used; the fertility used in growing crops must be replaced; and forests must be replanted as fast as they are cut. The grasslands, once restored, must never again be overgrazed; and never again should more birds or more mammals or more fishes be taken in a year than are warranted by the year's crop. If that one idea is seriously accepted and acted upon by every group and interest engaged in enterprises affecting the natural resources, the problem of conserving these resources for perpetual use will be largely solved.

4. Next on the list is the need of more and more research. The time will never come when it will be possible to rest secure in the knowledge that all conservation problems have been solved. The constantly shifting industrial, economic, and social factors in this country will always create new conservation problems—new problems in preservation, utilization, and restoration. That fact must be faced, and the only way it can be faced with any assurance is to have a sufficient force of technically trained men constantly applying themselves to the solution of conservation problems.

5. To provide for constantly better use of soil and water resources, the present trend toward restoration of environmental conditions, whether of forests or grasslands, marshes or lakes, must be carried much further. In adopting and executing such a program, America will only be paying for past mistakes. To realize errors is always painful and in many cases to make up for them is expensive, but if the people of this country are to get on a sustained basis of living,

a program of regulated use and full restoration must be adopted once and for all.

6. Environmental restoration (the putting of nature's forces to work for men) and limitation of the harvest to the crop produced have proved successful in increasing stocks of game and fishes. The trend is distinctly upward where these methods have been faithfully adhered to. The scope of rational management should be greater, and as the program continues the effect of increasing natural production will be cumulative. The most uncertain factor is not management itself but public support for a suitable and effective program that may be neither a spectacular performance nor a crusade. Each square mile of territory improved for wildlife will go on producing annual crops while other lands are being improved; each stream cleared of pollution will make its annual contribution of fishes while other waters are being restored. The conservation battle cannot be a short, sharp engagement, but must be grim, tenacious warfare—the sort that makes single gains and then consolidates these gains until renewed strength and a good opportunity make another advance possible.

It is yet to be demonstrated whether the conservation forces of America or the American people can wage that kind of fight. Much of our vaunted success in "conquering a continent in record time" has been in reality appalling wastefulness. Now America faces the hard task of putting to work natural forces in restoration and of staying tirelessly on the job throughout future years.

INDEX